A New Look at
Elementary School Science

NEW TRENDS IN CURRICULUM AND INSTRUCTION SERIES
JOHN U. MICHAELIS, editor

A New Look at Elementary School Science

Science Curriculum Improvement Study

ROBERT KARPLUS

Director, Science Curriculum Improvement Study
Professor of Physics
University of California, Berkeley

HERBERT D. THIER

Assistant Director, Science Curriculum
  Improvement Study
University of California, Berkeley

photographs by the authors

RAND MᶜNALLY & COMPANY   •   CHICAGO

RAND McNALLY EDUCATION SERIES
B. OTHANEL SMITH, *Advisory Editor*

NEW TRENDS IN CURRICULUM AND INSTRUCTION SERIES
Edited by JOHN U. MICHAELIS

Evans and Walker, *New Trends in the Teaching of English in Secondary Schools*

Karplus and Thier, *A New Look at Elementary School Science*

Michaelis, ed., *Teaching Units in the Social Sciences*
    Vol. I, *Early Grades*
    Vol. II, *Grades III-IV*
    Vol. III, *Grades V-VI*

Scott, *Trends in Elementary School Mathematics*

Smith and Cox, *New Strategies and Curriculum in Social Studies*

Copyright © 1969 by Rand McNally & Company
All rights reserved
Printed in U.S.A. by Rand McNally & Company
Library of Congress Catalogue Card Number 69:10585
Third Printing, 1970

To the late Richard E. Paulson,

Architect of Curriculum Revision

Preface

The postwar period has been characterized by increasing public interest in education at all levels. As a consequence of this interest, large study groups have been formed to improve course content in a range of academic disciplines for students of various ages. In order to be effective, the work of these groups has to become widely known, to be evaluated, and to be placed in the context of the educational program for which it was designed.

This book was written to furnish current information about the Science Curriculum Improvement Study to elementary school teachers and to students in teacher training. We hope it will also be of interest to school administrators who are reviewing the offerings of their schools and to parents who are concerned with new trends in instruction.

Our account describes the work of the project through the summer of 1966. As experimentation continues and feedback from trial teaching is gathered, the details of the program will change. Readers are invited to keep up to date with its development through the SCIS Newsletter, which is circulated free of charge upon request.

We should like to acknowledge our debt to Chester A. Lawson, Luke E. Steiner, and our other colleagues, past and present, in the Science Curriculum Improvement Study, in related curriculum projects, and in public education. Their contributions, advice, and stimulating criticisms have been of invaluable assistance.

ROBERT KARPLUS
HERBERT D. THIER

University of California, Berkeley
January 1967

Contents

Innovation in Science Education

SCIENTISTS LEND A HAND

Have you ever sorted out all the buttons accumulated in your sewing kit or all the screws and nuts in your hobby shop only to find one or two left over that "didn't fit"? In a way, this problem is similar to problems that face a scientist. He makes observations on his butterflies or his crystals or his atomic particles, and he must face the fact that some of his observations may not fit his expectations. Such an experience can be unsettling, but a scientist may use it as an opportunity that leads to new understanding and insight.

Creating in students the ability to cope with new and unexpected findings is a central objective of the innovators who have been experimenting with educational programs in the last fifteen years. After all, current views on the replacement of men by machines in industry and in agriculture imply that routine and repetitive work will and should be done mechanically. It is commonly hoped that man will then be free to pursue more stimulating work that requires imagination and adaptability.

In this situation, an additional burden is placed on the educational system. Not only traditions of knowledge and culture but also inquisitiveness and mental flexibility must be transmitted to future generations. The current ferment in education is a response to this challenge. Scholars, educators, and teachers are collaborating with the help of financial support from government agencies and private foundations as they undertake long-term intensive studies of educational problems in all curriculum areas.

Because individual disciplines, such as physics, chemistry, and biology, first appear in the high school curriculum and because the high school programs of many students have a college preparatory function, it is natural that new courses at the high school level should have been first developed. Scientists and mathematicians, who carried out the first studies, were soon joined by anthropologists, economists, linguists, and others. At the same time, the results obtained with the new programs indicated to many scientists and educational leaders that the pre-high school curricula also presented opportunities for improvement which they should exploit.

To determine whether the nation should undertake a concerted effort of curriculum improvement in elementary school science, the American Association for the Advancement of Science, with financial aid from the National Science Foundation, sponsored three regional conferences of scientists, teachers, school administrators, and psychologists to consider the following aspects of science instruction: present policies, practices, and materials; recent efforts to create new courses for senior high schools; and recent experiments in teaching young children. The conferences reached the following conclusions: Instruction in science should be a regular part of the curriculum from kindergarten through grade nine (and beyond, but the conference considered only these grades), a major effort should be undertaken, and this effort should involve improving both course materials and classroom teaching.

The report prepared by the steering committee for the conferences contains a discussion of many concerns that were aired by the conferences. Here only some points of substantial agreement will be listed briefly:

1. Science should be a basic part of general education for all students at the elementary and junior high schools levels.

2. Instruction at the elementary levels should deal in an organized way with science as a whole.

3. There must be a clear progression in the study of science from grade to grade.

4. There should be no single, national curriculum in science.

5. Science teaching should stress the spirit of discovery characteristic of science itself.

6. New instructional materials must be prepared for in-service and pre-service programs for science teachers.

7. The preparation of instructional materials will require the combined efforts of scientists, classroom teachers, and specialists in learning and teacher preparation.

8. There is great urgency to get started on the preparation of improved instructional materials for science.[1]

After this encouraging report was released in the spring of 1961, several study groups were set up along the lines suggested. The American Association for the Advancement of Science (AAAS) established a Commission on Science Education which is supervising the creation of new curriculum materials. The Commission also set up at the University of Maryland a clearing house for information concerning curriculum developments in elementary school science and mathematics. The annual bulletin of the clearing house may be consulted for current information about the projects, some with local support, some with foundation grants, which are active in this field. Here we shall mention only those study groups involved in the entire broad scope of elementary school science with foundation support. Educational Services Incorporated has formed the Elementary Science Study (ESS). At the University of Minnesota in Minneapolis, the Minnesota Mathematics and Science Teaching group (MINNEMAST) was organized. The University of Illinois added the School Science Curriculum Project (SSCP) to its Elementary School Science Project (Illinois-ESSP) which had been working on an astronomy course for some years. At the University of California, Berkeley, the Science Curriculum Improvement Study (SCIS) grew out of the Elementary School Science Project (UC-ESSP).

In organization and operation, the projects share certain common features. Ronald Gross, Assistant to the President of the Academy for Educational Development, has described these as follows:

> Diverse as they are in form and origin, the radical innovations now challenging American education share certain common elements.
> First, they have been initiated by distinguished university scholars rather than by professional educators .... In the heyday of progressive education, it was the educators, especially the educational psychologists, who took charge. In the current reform movement, the academic scholars made the first move. It is significant, though, that in trying to plant

---

[1] "Science Teaching in Elementary and Junior High Schools," reprinted from *Science*, CXXXIII, No. 3469 (June 23, 1961), 2019–24.

their specialities in the *terra incognita* of the ordinary class-room, the scholars found they needed all the light that contemporary psychology and related disciplines could provide.

Second, the major reforms have been created outside the educational establishment of state departments of education, teacher-training institutions, professional curriculum committees, and commercial textbook publishers. The curriculum revisions are national in scope and support, if not in actual application. . . .

Third, though the machinery of the educational establishment has been bypassed, the movement has won the support and enthusiasm of a great many practicing teachers and school administrators. Thus, the programs signal an unprecedented collaboration between academic scholars and schoolmen—the most hopeful outcome to date of the recent rapprochement of the two groups.

Fourth, the reformers have not merely issued dicta on what and how to teach. The scholars have gone into the classrooms; they have brought real children and seasoned teachers into their laboratories; and, together, they have created, tested, and revised materials and methods that will succeed in the schools.

Fifth, the most promising of the programs, whatever their particular form, draw from two broad streams of enlightenment: new understanding of the basic elements of each subject and new or freshly interpreted understanding of the capacity for learning inherent in youngsters.[2]

The projects also agree that science learning requires active involvement of the children, who perform experiments, make observations, and draw conclusions. In other words, the elementary school classrooms must become laboratories as well as study halls, and the school environment must be used for field studies as well as for recreation. Actually, this idea is not at all new in science education. It has been pointed out and emphasized many, many times in the past. Unfortunately, it was never implemented on a significant scale. By and large, what existed in the name of elementary science was a reading program.

As was anticipated by the AAAS study of 1960–61, however, the several projects are taking different approaches to the context or structure within which the pupils pursue their investigations. It will be possible, therefore, for communities that wish to use one of these programs to choose from among several alternatives

[2] Ronald Gross, "Two-Year-Olds Are Very Smart," *New York Times Magazine* (September 6, 1964), p. 39.

which are based on different theories of learning and which require different treatment by the teachers.

To make possible a comparison with the Science Curriculum Improvement Study, we shall here describe briefly some characteristics of SCIS and two other programs, one developed by the Elementary Science Study of Educational Services Inc. and the other under the auspices of the AAAS Commission on Science Education.

Children observe the dissolving process

The approach of the Science Curriculum Improvement Study, which will be described in much greater detail later, has been characterized by Robert Karplus.

> In order to reach the objective of scientific literacy, therefore, the science curriculum has to provide the pupils with experiences that are different from their usual ones. . . .
> A most interesting pedagogical question concerns the manner in which these experiences should be incorporated

into the teaching program. I hope it is clear that the experiences should be direct ones for the children, not told by the teacher or read in a book. . . . There is, however, the question of how much guidance the teacher or the book should provide for the children as they manipulate and observe, and how much discussion and review should follow the experience. How much verbalization should take place?

It is my belief that there should be substantial guidance and discussion. There should be an effort to relate the unusual experience to the more usual experience of which it represents an extreme case. In this way, the abstract concepts that are at the basis of the scientific point of view are built up. As the children make further observations, they will look at them more scientifically. The abstractions will form a link between their earlier experiences and later experiences, so that the children can bring their knowledge to bear in a systematic way. Perhaps the gulf between scientific thinking and common-sense thinking can be reduced!

Each lesson in the science program may fulfill one or both of these functions: to provide a new experience and to establish or reinforce an abstract concept. Connections between different lessons are created by use of the same phenomenon to illustrate different concepts and the use of the same concept to interpret different phenomena. The conceptual structure creates a context for the new experience that enables it to be assimilated rationally in relation to other experiences. One might say that the conceptual structure provides discipline for mental organization.[3]

In the pamphlet "An Introduction to the Elementary Science Study," the work and materials of that group are characterized as follows:

Learning theorists are quick to remind us that they do not yet fully understand which approach, which experiences, in which sequence produce the situation that makes an individual child or group of children respond. . . .

Confronted by such variables and unknowns, we feel that our approach should follow a mixed strategy—one that does not even pretend to be perfectly planned and leaves occasional decisions to chance and to the opportunities of the moment for a particular child, teacher, and classroom. . . . They are designed to appeal to all the senses, to the imagination and artistic instincts, and through the wordless experimental equipment as much as through the printed or spoken word. . . .

[3] Robert Karplus, "One Physicist Looks at Science Education," in *Intellectual Development: Another Look* (Washington, 1964), pp. 12–14.

Our program, therefore, is not bounded by disciplines nor fenced off by conventional frontiers. Our materials are developed simply as self-contained units, each providing experience in a particular exploration; each varying in subject matter, apparatus, level of complexity, and style of presentation; each guided by basic threads of scientific investigation—inquiry, evidence, instrumentation, measurement, classification, deduction.

Since ESS units develop around topics in which the basic threads of science stand out, the subject matter chosen is relatively unimportant—the path of a mealworm and the rise of a liquid both can be measured; living cells and wooden blocks both can be classified. Obviously we should not select only the bright and showy side of science; it seems to us that any subject should be acceptable provided it is not trivial and it relates to a child's natural environment.[4]

The AAAS-sponsored program, finally, is entitled "Science—A Process Approach." The foreword to the teachers' guide contains the following paragraphs:

There is a joy in the search for knowledge; there is excitement in learning about the workings of the physical universe and the biological world; there is intellectual power in the scientist's ways of asking questions and seeking answers to them. The first task and the central purpose of science education in the elementary school is to awaken in the child a sense of this joy and excitement and of the intellectual power of science.

The early parts of *Science—A Process Approach*, developed by the AAAS Commission on Science Education, provide instruction in science for the primary grades which emphasizes the development of competence in skills basic to further learning. These processes are called Observing, Recognizing and Using Number Relations, Measuring, Recognizing and Using Space/Time Relations, Classifying, Communication, Inferring, and Predicting. The child is introduced to a variety of content in acquiring these skills—he learns about plants and animals and rocks and weather and solutions of chemicals and the motions of objects. The content he learns is not systematically related to particular scientific disciplines, but is considered to be derived from more-or-less familiar objects and phenomena in the world around him. Our hope is that by the end of the third grade, the child who has been instructed by means of these exercises has acquired some important fundamental process skills, a good many basic scientific

---

[4] *Introduction to the Elementary Science Study* (Boston, 1965), pp. 7, 11.

concepts, and some organized knowledge about the natural world. . . .

These instructional materials consist of descriptions for the teacher of exercises drawn from a variety of science fields. They are arranged as an orderly progression of learning experiences. The objectives, the student performance expected by the time each exercise is completed, are clearly specified. To ensure that these objectives have been attained, an associated appraisal exercise is provided.[5]

The interested reader is urged to examine in detail the course materials produced by these three groups and by the others. He will then find a variety of approaches to the curriculum. For example, the units produced by the SCIS and the Parts written by the AAAS form a complete and integrated curriculum, while the ESS is creating self-contained units that may be fashioned into a curriculum by local teaching groups. He will also find that there are significant differences in emphasis on the three elements—concepts, phenomena, processes—which make up the science course. Thus, the ESS stresses the child's involvement with the phenomena and is confident that he will thereby gain practice with the processes and achieve understanding of valuable concepts even though these are not made explicit. The SCIS stresses the concepts and phenomena, with process learnings an implicit by-product of the children's experimentation, discussion, and analyses. The AAAS stresses the child's practice with the processes and uses the phenomena only as vehicles and the concepts as tools. An added difference is that the AAAS program attempts to appraise the children's progress more systematically and in greater detail than do the others.

This completes our general review of the current state of elementary science education. It is clear from the foregoing that the possibility of a single national curriculum being imposed by the federally sponsored projects is out of the question. Further variety is being added by the commercial publishing houses, which are becoming more bold about emphasizing the dependence of science learning on active experimentation. Undoubtedly their authors, some of whom are participating in curriculum studies, will incorporate into their series what to them seems most promising among new developments.

[5] *Science—A Process Approach* (Washington: American Association for the Advancement of Science, 1965), Foreword.

ORIGIN OF THE SCIENCE CURRICULUM
IMPROVEMENT STUDY

Let us now turn to the history of the Science Curriculum Improvement Study. It was established in the winter of 1962 by Robert Karplus, a professor of theoretical physics at the University of California in Berkeley, as a result of his work with the Elementary School Science Project (ESSP) at that university. This experience had led Professor Karplus to the conclusion that elementary school science had not only to be simplified but organized on a drastically different basis from the usual logical subject-matter presentations to which the university scientist is accustomed.

The ESSP itself began because of a fortuitous combination of circumstances during 1957 and 1958. Professor Karplus' oldest children were entering school, and they interested their father in working with their classes. Professor Leo Brewer, a University of California chemist who had been concerned with secondary school teaching problems, also had young children entering school. Finally, the National Science Foundation, which had been supporting scientific research projects, decided to support the development of new high school physics and chemistry courses and showed a willingness to explore curriculum reform in the elementary schools also. Accordingly, professors Karplus and Brewer secured the cooperation of the College of Education at Berkeley and together with professors Arthur Pardee in biochemistry and Lloyd F. Scott in elementary education submitted a proposal for "A Study of Course Content Improvement in Elementary School Science." The proposal was introduced by the following statement of the problem to be attacked:

It is already clear today that science plays a major role in all human activities, ranging from everyday living to world politics. It is also clear that science will continue to play an increasingly important role in every individual's life, whether he may have chosen science as a profession or not. In order to prepare an individual for life in a society where science plays such an important role, one would expect science to be prominent in any curriculum.

Considerable activity by various professional groups is presently directed toward the improvement of high school mathematics and specialized science courses. It is probably in the elementary grades, however that the presentation of science is most important and can reach the largest fraction of school children. Since the attitudes of students towards science are strongly influenced by their experience with this subject in the lower grades, it is essential that those who have the ability to continue with more advanced work form an interest in doing so, while those who cannot or should not go on are nevertheless left with an understanding that will enable them to be scientifically literate citizens. The specialized science courses that are offered in high school and beyond are largely elective and most non-college-preparatory students receive only a year of general science.

One of the most serious aspects of science education in the elementary and secondary schools is the gap that appears to exist between the concept of science held by scientists and that held by teachers, school administrators, and school textbook writers. For the latter, science is a body of facts or "right answers" which must be instilled in the students; for the former it is the wrestling with problems and apparent contradictions that arise from the observation of natural phenomena. To a large extent this gap is due to the lack of attention on the part of those in the field of science to the problem of science education. As a consequence, elementary school curricula usually lack continuity in the presentation of science and fail to demonstrate the unity of science.

To remedy this situation we propose to undertake a study whose results will aid in the development of an adequate science teaching program both for the elementary schools through the eighth grade and also for teacher training institutions.

The program of extending to the elementary level the work in progress for high school courses is made difficult by the fact that the pupil's mastery of reading, writing, and arithmetic as tools is far from complete. A still more serious problem, however, is the almost universal practice that makes a single teacher responsible for handling all subject matter. There are unquestionably educational advantages in such an arrangement and we do not wish to criticize. Nevertheless, it has the consequence that almost all teachers who have some training in science become specialist teachers in high school, while most of the elementary school teachers have had only the minimal required contact with science through high school and college courses which themselves are obsolete in many respects. Any improvement of the preparatory courses will eventually have a highly beneficial effect on the prospective teachers.

With the support of the grant from the National Science

Foundation, three science units were prepared and tried in the school year 1959–60. The units were entitled *Coordinates, Force,* and *What Am I?* Though the teaching of "Coordinates" and "Force" generated some enthusiasm, talks with the teachers and pupils revealed serious misconceptions and certain weaknesses. Analysis of the whole trial teaching experience led Professor Karplus to raise three questions. First, how can one create a learning experience that achieves a secure connection between the pupils' intuitive attitudes and the concepts of the modern scientific point of view? Second, how can one determine what the children have learned? Third, how can one communicate with the teacher so that the teacher can in turn communicate with the pupils?

In the spring of 1960, Professor Karplus had an opportunity to familiarize himself with the point of view children take toward natural phenomena and to develop tentative answers to the first of the three questions. It became possible for him to conduct classes in a first, a second, and a fourth grade on a regular schedule twice a week. The concepts of relative motion, force, system, momentum, and atomic structure were introduced, and their acceptance by the children was explored in the lessons.

The results of this study were interpreted and developed further by Professor Karplus while he was on sabbatical leave as Guggenheim Fellow and Fulbright Research Scholar in Physics at the University of Vienna. When he returned to the United States in the fall of 1961, Professor Karplus had formulated a plan for the beginning of science instruction in the primary grades. As in the first trial two years earlier, he planned to stress the pupils' learning by making their own observations of experiments in the classroom. He planned also, however, to teach them to interpret their observations in a more analytical way than children do without special instruction. To this end he arranged to teach regularly in a second grade class at the Berkwood School, Berkeley, California.

During part of the school year, J. Myron Atkin, Professor of Education at the University of Illinois and co-director of Illinois-ESSP, was in Berkeley and helped to orient Professor Karplus to some of the problems faced by teachers and pupils in elementary school classes. Together, Professors Atkin and Karplus formulated a theory of guided discovery in which they pointed out the role played in discovery by the preconceptions or "mental set" of the observer. These preconceptions determine which generalization a child can infer from his experiences. If the child is to build modern scientific concepts, he has to look at his experiments and interpret them from the modern scientific point of view. In his experimental teaching, Professor Karplus tried to develop this point of view with his pupils.

The program began with a consideration of the material objects that are involved in an experiment. Such a collection of objects that are of interest at one time is called a *system*. The component parts of the system are called *objects*. Finally, the word *interaction* is used to designate the mutual influence of objects which results in changes in the appearance of the system. Other concepts in the program were fields of force, equilibrium, the approach of systems to equilibrium, and relative motion and configuration, which were studied with the help of an artificial observer called "Mr. O."

Despite the fact that most of the experiments involved familiar effects of familiar objects, the new way of thinking about them was

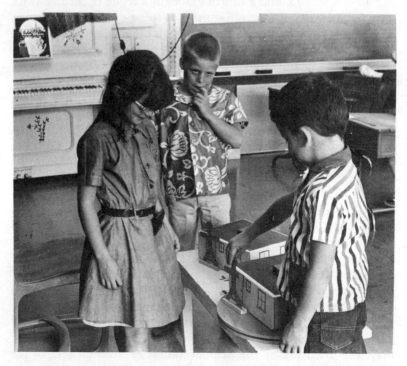

Mr. "O" is used to develop an understanding of configuration

stimulating to the children. After one lesson in which Mr. O was used to describe relative motion, one little girl concluded, "It isn't always the way it looks." Later in the year, the children decided that many processes of change in a system eventually come to an end when the system reaches equilibrium. One boy, however, commented to Professor Karplus, "I know something that will go on forever. You will keep talking forever." At this point it was appropriate to change to a new topic.

The novel direction being taken by this course of study made it desirable to continue the investigation as a project separated from the UC-ESSP. The name Science Curriculum Improvement Study was therefore adopted.

During the summer of 1962 Professor Karplus accepted an invitation to work with the Elementary Science Study of Educational Services Incorporated. The investigations he carried out made it clear to him that children need time to explore an experimental system at their own pace and with their own preconceptions. Only after this has happened is it wise to introduce a more analytical or sophisticated point of view, with the help of which the same system can be re-examined more scientifically.

For the following year, it became possible to try out the modified approach in several public school classes. The Science Curriculum Improvement Study was temporarily headquartered at the University of Maryland, where Professor Karplus served as Visiting Professor of Physics. A number of new staff members joined the project. Most important, Dr. Herbert D. Thier, Assistant Superintendent of Schools in Falls Church, Virginia, became a consultant and later assistant director of SCIS. He experimented with the new teaching program in some primary-grade classes of his district. Another consultant, Mrs. Doris Hadary, Assistant Professor of Chemistry at American University and formerly a coordinator for the BSCS high school biology courses, worked with fifth- and sixth-grade students in observing and interpreting evidence of interaction of living organisms with their environment.

The laboratory approach the children were permitted to take was much appreciated by the older pupils. They expressed strong enthusiasm for the science classes in which they were able to experiment and to make their own observations of the evolution of oxygen by green plants, the growth of micro organisms, and many other phenomena. The younger pupils, of course, were less eloquent in their responses. They also, however, exhibited great fascination with such simple tasks as sorting a mixed-up collection of plastic buttons and with more demanding tasks such as mixing plaster of paris, neutralizing acid with base, and keeping a record of their own weight over a period of several weeks.

It appeared that a partial answer was now available to the question of how one can create a learning experience that achieves a secure connection between the pupils' intuitive attitudes and the concepts of the modern scientific point of view. Attack on the other two questions was furthered by an opportunity to cooperate with a larger project in the summer of 1963 when Professor Karplus accepted an invitation to serve as co-director for science of MINNEMAST. This project, founded and directed by mathematician Paul Rosenbloom of the University of Minnesota, had been concentrating on improved mathematics teaching but was expanding its efforts to include science as well.

For eight weeks, thirty-five scientists, teachers, and psychologists from colleges, high schools, and elementary schools were assembled at the University of Minnesota in Minneapolis. The samples of teaching programs that were prepared strongly emphasized pupil experimentation, observation, and interpretation.

In the fall of 1963, the Science Curriculum Improvement Study resumed its work at the University of California to explore the concept of science education based on communicating scientific literacy. The scope and sequence of the curriculum were to be determined by the structure of science, the maturity of the pupils, and the pupils' preconceptions. Individual lessons were to be organized according to the discovery method of concept development and the needs of the learners. These considerations will be described in detail in later chapters of this book.

THE PROCESS OF CURRICULUM DEVELOPMENT

Here we shall discuss the procedures that are being used by SCIS in the development of the teaching program. As was pointed out already, the experimental work of the Science Curriculum Improvement Study during the years 1961–63 laid the basis for the production of a coordinated primary-grade physical science program. The central objective is to lead children to approach the observation and analysis of natural phenomena by thinking in terms of systems of interacting objects or components. At the same time, the activities in the classroom are intended to give the children experience with a wide variety of natural phenomena, to develop many manipulative skills in the carrying out of experiments, and to furnish opportunities for recording the results of observation.

Observing evidence of interaction in a thermometer-ice system

Even though the science program is being subdivided into units, a unit cannot be developed in isolation from the others because of the units' strong interdependence on the conceptual level. This conceptual interdependence is one of the distinguishing characteristics of the SCIS program, and it appears to be the most significant aspect for the intellectual growth of the pupils. It does, however, necessitate a rather complicated trial procedure which depends on the availability at each grade level of pupils who have had experience with the SCIS program in earlier grades.

The work on one unit progresses roughly as follows:

1. Preparation of a teaching plan and design of experiments.
2. Exploratory teaching in public schools by SCIS staff members.
3. Completion of unit, teaching materials, teachers' guide, student manuals, and equipment kits.
4. Classroom trial of units by SCIS staff and by regular teachers in four Berkeley area laboratory schools (one to two years).
5. Revision and reconsideration of the unit in the light of experience, with additional exploratory teaching by SCIS staff members.
6. Second classroom trial by regular teachers (one to two years).
7. Revision and preliminary commercial publication by D. C. Heath & Co.
8. Classroom trial in several centers across the United States (two to three years).

It will be noticed that classroom feedback is to be incorporated at three stages (points 3, 5, and 7). The closely supervised teaching in very few local schools is a most significant source of information. Questionnaires answered by the teachers and evaluation meetings held with the teachers supplement the information that is obtained when SCIS staff members make observations in the classroom. It often happens that this feedback from one unit suggests changes in several units. The unit being tested is directly involved, but all the preceding units also may have to be reconsidered because they frequently present excellent opportunities for introducing an experience or idea that appeared to be lacking. If it is true that science has a structure, then the teaching program should develop an idea in the context that reveals this structure adequately and not only when there is a need to apply the idea to solve a problem that arises.

The important and often most difficult decisions that have to be made in each unit have to do with the fact that some things can be discovered by children doing experiments but some cannot. These latter are the man-made constructs in terms of which he thinks about natural phenomena. The creator of a unit must have clearly in mind what constructs are already available to the pupils (among the preconceptions which were mentioned earlier) and what constructs must be introduced to enable the pupils to make the discoveries potentially derivable from the experimental observations. As was said previously, the order and context in which the constructs are introduced are also important, because they determine the hierarchical arrangement that is established. Sometimes experience with later units suggests strongly that a construct was "missing" or was understood in too narrow a fashion.

The preceding paragraph may be illustrated by the story of one problem that had to be solved: In what order should the concepts of *interaction* and *system* be introduced? The first decision (exploration 1961) was to introduce *system* as a grouping of objects with no other criteria and *interaction* as a relation between objects. This approach led to much random association of objects into systems. A second attempt (exploration 1962, trial teaching 1963, 1964) was to introduce *interaction* first and then *system* as a group of interacting objects. This procedure clearly differentiated between *systems* and *sets*, but it also created considerable rigidity: The pupils tended to focus on the systems while the objects were interacting, but tended to reject systems of objects that were not currently interacting. Now, a system is defined as an object or objects with an interesting relation to one another or to an observer. The relation may involve interaction among the objects or it may involve their placement and motion. Since the systems concept is broader than the interactions concept, the trial unit *Interaction and Systems* (1963) has been revised into two separate units, *Systems* (1966) and *Interaction* (1966), to be used in that order. Trial teaching experience with this approach has shown that it, too, has shortcomings, in that the consideration of systems for their own sake just tends to be abstract and not very interesting. The present plans for revision, therefore, are to delete the separate *Systems* unit, and to introduce the systems concept in an introductory portion of the *Interaction* unit.

Because of the integrated nature of the SCIS program, the trial and revision procedures are quite time-consuming. The first-grade program, for instance, may have to be reviewed in the light of work done by the first graders when they come to second or third grade or even later. There is also a reason for conducting classroom trials for more than one year between revisions. During the first year, the ideas and procedures of a unit are so novel to many teachers that their reactions are not indicative of actual difficulties in pedagogical design. Only on repetition are the teachers able to plan instruction satisfactorily because then they know what range of behaviors to expect from the pupils.

II

Theoretical Background
for Science Education

WHY ELEMENTARY SCHOOL SCIENCE?

Just how important a part science teaching can and should play in the elementary school has not been generally recognized until recently. Previously it was thought that the children's ability for rational thinking was only adequate for a program that emphasized the basic skills of reading, writing, and arithmetic. Other areas, such as science and social studies, were taught in a context of activities oriented around the basic skills. In the meantime, children's thinking was expected to develop spontaneously until, in high school and college, the subject-matter fields could become significant parts of the curriculum. But the development of many pupils does not keep pace with the school's expectations. They become frustrated by academic work in high school and lose interest in education.

The older view of the development of children held that the early grades were, in part, a period of waiting for maturity. Today we recognize that intellectual stimulation during the formative years is as important as native endowment in determining the future achievement of each child. Such a modern view permits the elementary school to make a greater, more vital contribution than ever before. This re-evaluation will in time affect all areas of the curriculum. However, its impact on mathematics and science programs is being felt earliest.

Let us explain briefly how science is related to intellectual development. The present content of science consists of concepts and relationships that mankind has abstracted from the observation of natural phenomena over the centuries. This content is the outcome of a long, slow process. During the elementary school years, boys and girls are engaged in precisely the same kind of abstracting process with respect to their own natural environment. They accumulate experiences, and their thinking undergoes a gradual transition from the concrete to the abstract. Yet it has been found that there are many gaps and misconceptions in such spontaneously developed understandings.

It is, therefore, the responsibility of the schools to guide the children's development by providing them with particularly informative and suggestive experiences as a base for their abstractions. At the same time, the children must be provided with a conceptual framework that permits them to perceive phenomena

Sorting nuts and washers introduces Kindergarten children to categorization and grouping

in a more meaningful way. This framework will also help them to integrate their inferences into generalizations of greater value than the ones they would form if left to their own devices.

The awareness just described is due in large part to the work of the Swiss psychologist Jean Piaget, whose views are presented in an article in the Appendix (p. 170). His ideas have been elaborated and applied to problems in education by American scholars such as Millie Almy, Jerome Bruner, J. McV. Hunt, and Celia Stendler, among others. This school of thought has two related central ideas: (1) Children's intellectual capacity passes through a number of qualitatively contrasting stages before adulthood. (2) A child's interaction with his environment plays a very significant role in his transition from one stage to the next.

There is some variation from author to author in the specification of the successive stages, but they all agree that children's modes of thinking differ drastically from those used by adults. Piaget, for example, separates the development into four stages. Only in the last of these, called the stage of formal operations, is the child able to reason like an adult about the relationships and implications of verbal statements. In the next-to-the-last stage, that of concrete operations, the child is able to reason by using operations, such as classification, serial ordering, and time sequencing, on objects, but he cannot yet apply such operations to verbally expressed hypotheses. Preceding this is a stage which is pre-operational: Objects exist and their present appearance can be described by the child, but changes with time or as a result of physical transformations are not comprehended by him. During infancy, finally, there is a sensory-motor, pre-verbal stage during which the permanent existence of objects and simple spatial relations are established through a combination of visual and kinesthetic explorations.

A few examples, which the reader may verify by working with children, will serve to illustrate this outline. Children at the pre-operational stage, for instance, are unable to use conservation reasoning: If liquid is poured from one container into another one of different shape, the pre-operational child will think there is more in one than in the other; if a number of coins are rearranged from a long line into a circle or a heap, he will think there is a greater number in one arrangement than in the other.

Children at the stage of concrete operations can use conservation logic. That is, they recognize that an amount or number stays the same if nothing is added or removed, even though the appearance presented changes. In other words, they recognize that the height of liquid in a narrow container may compensate for the width of the same amount of liquid in a wide container. They can also serialize objects according to one property, and they know that if object A exceeds object B, and object B exceeds object C, then object A will exceed object C (transitivity). They however, are not yet able to reason about abstractions as effectively as they can reason about concrete operations. Even though they can divide a whole into parts $(1 \div 4 = \frac{1}{4})$, they cannot divide by fractions $(1 \div \frac{1}{4} = 4)$, an operation which has no concrete analogue. Similarly, they cannot compare the energy of a heavy object a small distance above the floor and the energy of a light object a great distance above the floor. In other words, they do not recognize in what way energy is a composite of height and weight, even though they do recognize that the amount of liquid in a container is a composite of height and cross-sectional area.

The time of appearance of the stages varies with the individual. The pre-operational stage begins about age two; the stage of concrete operations, between five and ten; the stage of formal operations, between ten and fifteen. It is also known that an individual

Exploring conservation of liquid

does not suddenly pass from one stage to the next. Instead, the development takes place in some areas first and then in others, so that a six-year-old child may be in the stage of concrete operations with respect to the number of elements in a set, but he may still be pre-operational with respect to the amount of liquid in a container. Furthermore, it is clear from work with college students and adults that the ability to reason on the formal level, which does become established in most of them, is not adequate to encompass the results or thinking or attitudes of modern science.

To plan educational programs which advance children's intellectual development, one must know what factors influence it. Besides physiological maturation, on which the school cannot exert any influence, the two most significant factors appear to be an active physical and mental exploration of reality and social interaction with parents, teachers, and peers. The former enriches the child's experience with regard to the objects and phenomena which exist and the actions or control the child can exert over them. The latter stimulates review of the experience and representation of it by words or symbols—both essential steps in dealing with abstractions. Of course, the level on which communication with others takes place must be appropriate to the developmental stage of the participating children. Hunt has summarized the situation in the following statement:

> The problem for the management of child development is to find out how to govern the encounters that children have with their environments to foster both an optimally rapid rate of intellectual development and a satisfying life.[6]

What about the often-heard recommendation that science instruction be postponed until the youngsters have reached the intellectual maturity of the middle teens? At this stage, unfortunately, educational efforts reach only that fraction of the student body which is favorably disposed toward science because of earlier positive experience at home or at school. For the others, many of whom form a strong dislike for science, it is too late. Their spontaneous intellectual development just does not keep pace with the expectation of the school, or does not proceed in the direction of modern science.

The significance of an elementary school science program has been described by many educators who have concerned themselves

[6] J. McV. Hunt, *Intelligence and Experience* (New York, 1961), pp. 362–63.

with the broad objectives of science courses. Nevertheless, there is general agreement that current teaching practices do not meet the pupils' needs. There are probably two reasons for this state of affairs. One is a conflict in goals—science educators advocate mental flexibility and independence while teaching practice seeks to transmit traditions of knowledge and culture, traditions that are certified by authorities and are not to be questioned. The second reason is the conflict, described at the beginning of this chapter, in psychological and educational theory, with educational practice reflecting a view (fixed intelligence/pre-determined development) that robs science teaching of its developmental significance. It is not surprising, therefore, that one great weakness of current practice seems to be an almost exclusive reliance on textbooks and other such authoritative sources of information. These sources for science learning, however, are quite impotent compared to the direct experiences that nourish the pupils' intellectual development of "common sense" rationality. Instead of guiding this development in the direction of modern scientific understanding, therefore, the present-day science courses create a second, separate, relatively abstract structure which is not used outside the school situation and which eventually atrophies.

These remarks must not be interpreted to mean that a pupil can learn only what he himself observes; the world is too complicated to permit that. It does mean, however, that the early years of school should provide a highly diversified program based heavily on concrete experiences. The difficult part, which is often overlooked, is that the concrete experiences must be presented in a context that helps to build a conceptual framework for operations with abstractions. Then, and only then, will the early learning form a base for the assimilation of experiences that come later—experiences that may involve either direct observation or verbal and pictorial reports of observations made by others. In other words, to be able to use information obtained by others, to benefit from the reading of textbooks and other references that present information in abstract form, the individual must have a conceptual structure and a means of communication that enable him to interpret the information as though he had obtained it himself. We will call this functional understanding of scientific concepts "scientific literacy". It should be the principal objective of the elementary school science program.

THE NATURE AND STRUCTURE OF SCIENCE

In the previous sections, it was pointed out that the development of science bears a resemblance to the intellectual growth of children. We then presented a discussion of child development. In this section we shall elaborate on the nature and structure of science so as to clarify the meaning of "scientific literacy."

The present content of science consists of concepts and relationships that mankind has abstracted from the observation of natural phenomena over the centuries. This overall evolutionary process has been marked by occasional major and minor scientific revolutions which re-oriented entire fields of endeavor. Examples are the Copernican revolution in astronomy, the conception of natural selection by Darwin, and the introduction of quantum theory into atomic physics. The result is a conceptual structure and a point of view with which the scientist approaches his work.

Let us briefly consider in an overly simplified way how a scientist may proceed. From a number of similar observations the scientist formulates an hypothesis about the behavior of a class of objects in the kind of situations he has studied. He then continues to make observations in further situations to which he expects his hypothesis to apply. If the behavior always turns out to be consistent with his expectation, the hypothesis is confirmed and thereafter may be called a law of nature. If the behavior turns out to be contrary to his expectation, the hypothesis in its original form must be abandoned.

As an example, think of a ball released without support which falls to the ground. After additional observations (the dropping to the ground of pieces of wood, a feather, and a glass bowl), we are ready to formulate an hypothesis: All objects fall to the ground when released without support. We now continue the experiment. Eventually, we release a helium-filled balloon and find that it does not drop; instead, it rises. That is the end of this hypothesis. Can we modify it successfully? The "hypothesis of universal gravity" could be changed to "all objects fall to the ground when released without support in a vacuum." This statement is still sensible only near the earth or another large heavenly body. In space, far from the earth, "falling to the ground" is meaningless because there is no "ground."

This simple description has glossed over two decisions that were made. One was the judgment as to what constituted "similar" observations. In our example, for instance, it is possible to consider the balloon to be so different from the other objects that its behavior should not have been considered relevant to the "hypothesis of universal gravity." Also, there is the question of whether the heavenly bodies—the moon, for instance—are objects to which the hypothesis is to apply. The second is the judgment as to what aspects of the observations are to be compared. Again, in our example, are we concerned that the bodies moved when they were released or that they ultimately came to rest? Before an ordinary scientific study can take place, these two types of questions must be answered. Usually the answers are implicitly assumed and agreed upon by the members of the scientific community and constitute what we may call the "scientific point of view." One element of this point of view is the supposition that natural phenomena are reproducible—that under a given set of conditions the same behavior will ensue. Other elements have to do with the form of an acceptable explanation of a phenomenon. Occasionally, however, new observations create serious difficulties in understanding when they are considered from the current point of view. Then there is the need for bold and imaginative thinking to develop a new point of view that shows more promise of being able to deal successfully with the known phenomena. Eventually this may become the accepted "scientific point of view."

Science is, therefore, never complete. There are always some unanswered questions, some unexpected phenomena. These may eventually be resolved within the accepted structure of science, or they may force a revision of the fundamental point of view from which the phenomena were interpreted. Progress in science comes from the discovery of a new phenomenon and from the invention of novel interpretations that illuminate in a new way the new and the well-known phenomena. Scientific truth is, therefore, not absolute and permanent; rather, it is in accordance with the facts as currently known. Without this qualification, the statement that scientists seek the truth is misleading. It is better to say that scientists seek understanding.

It is worthwhile to consider what gives credibility to statements made by scientists. Some are definitions, such as "Photosynthesis is the conversion of light energy into chemical energy by green plants." This assertion cannot be false, because it describes the meaning of photosynthesis. The worst that could happen with a definition is that the word does not correspond to reality, such as "A *time machine* is a device that can place its operator in the past or future."

Other statements, often called assumptions, axioms, or postulates in logic, are taken on faith. For example, we have pointed out that scientists accept the existence of a real world and the reproducibility of natural phenomena. Still other propositions are deduced by logical reasoning from definitions and axioms. The definitions, "$1 + 1 = 2$" and "$1 + 1 + 1 + 1 = 4$," of 2 and 4, for instance, can be combined to yield the conclusion "$2 + 2 = 4$". There is flexibility in such a system of statements in that we could have used "$1 + 1 = 2$" and "$2 + 2 = 4$" as definitions to deduce "$1 + 1 + 1 + 1 = 4$." The content of these is the same as before, but the logical structure is different.

Finally, there are statements derived by reasoning from all the types mentioned in combination with empirical evidence. For example, "The same side of the moon always faces the earth" does not follow from the definition of moon and general assumptions but is based on direct observation. Other assertions of this kind are based indirectly on observation, such as "cigarettes cause lung cancer." Since the scientist gathers and interprets empirical evidence, statements of this last kind play an especially important role. When they are well established and of general validity, they may be called laws of nature. Any statement based directly or indirectly on empirical evidence, however, may be questioned, for the evidence may, in someone's judgment, be inadequate.

In the previous discussion of the nature of science, reference has been made to scientific concepts and to a structure of science. It is now necessary to elaborate on the significance of these terms. One way to approach this problem is to inquire how a scientist gives meaning to a concept in such a way that its relevance to the study of natural phenomena is assured. The use of a system of dictionary definitions is clearly inadequate, for a dictionary always gives the meaning of one word in terms of other words. Ultimately, therefore, as one pursues the definitions of the definitions, the dictionary will exhaust the language. It must either include some undefined terms or its definitions must become circular. In ordinary usage this limitation of the dictionary presents no serious difficulty because its users have a fund of understanding which makes it unnecessary for them to pursue the definitions of definitions indefinitely. The dictionary is helpful because it serves to explain the unknown in terms of the known. This kind of common knowledge of a culture enables its literate members to use language for communication about concrete and abstract matters.

In a way, the scientific community may be considered a culture within which communication is possible because its members are "scientifically literate" and share a point of view or fund of common understanding. Special attention has to be devoted to the fund of common understanding, however, because it occasionally becomes an obstacle to progress and must be revised. Scientists, therefore, have developed the technique of operational definitions to specify the meaning of many terms in such a way that their connection with physical reality becomes part of the definition. Put in another way, words may be defined by other words, but they may also be defined by appeal to physical operations with concrete objects. These physical operations and concrete objects, then, are demonstrated and are not defined by mere words.

As an illustrative example, let us consider the concepts *vertical*, *horizontal*, and *right angle* which are related through the experimental fact that a vertical line is at right angles to a horizontal surface. Possible structural approaches to these three concepts are summarized in Table 1. In the diagram, operationally defined concepts are enclosed in solid boxes, concepts with formal definitions are in dashed boxes, and laws empirically discovered, are in ovals. It was necessary to define two other concepts, *straight line* and *equality of angles*, in order to construct an operational definition of *right angle*.

It should be noted that conceptual structure C, Table 1, makes possible a new kind of relationship. The three independently defined concepts—vertical, horizontal, and right angle—may be compared empirically, and it can be discovered that they are related and that the vertical direction makes a right angle with a horizontal plane. The operational approach, therefore, has two advantages: The concepts are given a concrete meaning and relationships among the concepts can be discovered by experiment. It should be added that one can usually give several operational definitions of the same term. Here again, the equivalence of these definitions can be discovered by experiment.

In closing this section, we point out that, as illustrated in Table 1, one can construct alternate conceptual structures with the same

Table 1

CASE A. Define vertical: direction of a free plumb line at rest.
Define horizontal: direction of a free water surface at rest.
Define right angle: the angle between the vertical and horizontal.

CASE B. Define vertical (see Case A).
Define straight line: matches a stretched string.
Define equal angles: angles that match when superposed.
Define right angle: draw two intersecting straight lines on a given (flat) board, so that four equal angles are produced. Each angle is a right angle.
Define horizontal: the surface at right angles to the vertical.

CASE C. Define vertical: (see Case A).
Define horizontal: (see Case A).
Define right angle: (see Case B).
Law of Nature: vertical and horizontal make a right angle.

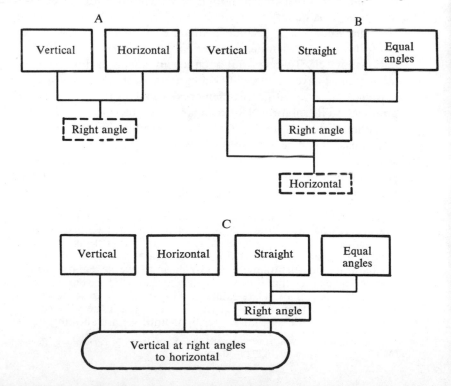

concepts. There is some freedom as to which terms are taken as starting points and which ones are derived from these by operations or by verbal definitions. The choice is dictated by considerations outside the realm of science. For example, one may desire an efficient structure in which there is a minimum number of operationally defined terms and a maximum number of derived terms. Or one may wish to teach young children. In that case, one would strive for a maximum number of operationally defined terms and a minimum number of derived ones. Other considerations may lead to a compromise between these extremes.

THE SCIENCE CURRICULUM

We now turn to consider the implications of the preceding remarks for the science curriculum. The teaching objective is to give the students sufficient knowledge and experience so that they will be able to have some understanding of scientific work being carried out by others, even though they themselves do not become scientists. This quality we have called scientific literacy. It is clear that the student can become acquainted with the experience of wrestling with a scientific problem only by carrying out investigations himself. To carry out such an investigation, however, the student must have an adequate background so that he can sense the existence of a scientific problem and can construct a tentative approach to its solution. This means he must be able to look at the potential problem situation from the "scientific point of view."

There is, of course, a reason why most adults develop a common-sense natural philosophy which does not correspond to the scientific point of view. Many aspects of the natural environment are taken for granted and never questioned. Benjamin Lee Whorf has observed

... if a rule has absolutely no exceptions, it is not recognized as a rule or as anything else; it is then part of the background of experience of which we tend to remain unconcious. Never having experienced anything to contrast to it, we cannot isolate it and formulate it as a rule until we so enlarge our experience and expand our base of reference that we encounter an interruption of its regularity. The situation is somewhat analogous to that of not missing the water 'till the well runs dry, or not realizing that we need air until we are choking.[7]

[7] Benjamin Lee Whorf, "Science and Linguistics," *Technology Review* (M.I.T.), XLII (April 1940), 229–30.

Since the scientific point of view is based on more diversified experience than that of one individual, many rules are established that seem tautologous when applied to the restricted range of easily accessible phenomena. Suppose, for example, the teacher holds a block, releases it, and it drops. Why did it drop? Most pupils will say, "Because you let go." This answer is the only sensible one for terrestrial pupils. Gravitation is part of the background against which they view experience. Deviation from the normal behavior, e.g., the block's not falling, is noted and ascribed to a cause—the hand holds the block. When the cause ceases to act, normal behavior is resumed.

It is futile, therefore, to tell children that free objects fall down because of an "earth pull" called gravity. This concept has no significant operational meaning since it is only a new name for a familiar experience. A more promising teaching approach is one in which children can observe variation in an effect such that the presence or absence of the effect can be associated with the presence or absence of a gravitational interaction. The most direct demonstration would involve massive laboratory objects, such as the buckets of sand used by Cavendish, but the effect is probably too small to be produced reliably in an elementary school classroom. The more usual procedure has been to compare terrestrial with astronomical observations and to recognize that the effect of gravity decreases as the distance from the earth increases. An alternate technique is to create artificial gravity fields by means of rotating turntables. Plumb lines attached to a rotating phonograph turntable, for example, vary in their orientation and therefore define a host of "vertical" directions at various places on the turntable. This phenomenon furnishes a clear contrast with the uniform gravity in the children's environment.

In order to reach the objective of scientific literacy, therefore, the science curriculum has to provide the pupils with experiences that are different from their usual ones. The differences may have to do with the substances that are manipulated. These substances can be hard or soft, elastic or unelastic, more dense or less dense, brittle or ductile, chemically active or inert. For instance, most objects commonly used have a specific gravity between 0.8 and 3. Polystyrene foam pieces and cast iron skillets, whose densities fall outside this range, create quite an impression because of their unusual densities.

Another type of experience is based on instruments or devices that may extend the range of the senses. Magnifying glasses, microscopes, and telescopes permit visual observation and comparisons that are out of the ordinary. Thermometers, spring scales, voltmeters, graduated cylinders, and stroboscopes make possible the discovery of many quantitative equivalences.

A third kind of experience has to do with unusual environmental conditions. The sensation of apparent weightlessness in an orbiting satellite would obviously be very interesting but will be outside the reach of elementary school pupils for some time to come. An express elevator with sudden starts and stops is the closest most of us will come to weightlessness. A rotating platform such as a merry-go-round is a "floor" on which the laws of nature are different from the customary ones. A completely dark space and a space illuminated with light of one color lead to a re-examination of the role and properties of light.

A fourth kind of experience, finally, is based on the observation of living organisms. Here motion pictures may have to substitute for some direct experience because many organisms are not commonly available or cannot usually be observed under controlled conditions. Yet certain animals exhibit characteristic behavior patterns in an extreme form that calls attention to similar behavior in other organisms where it is too subtle to be noticed easily. That animals exhibit what is called "behavior" is already a very significant learning, for example.

A most interesting pedagogical question concerns the manner in which these experiences should be incorporated into the teaching program. It is clear that the experiences should be direct ones for the children, not told by the teacher or read in a book. To see sketches of a snail or to hear someone tell about feeling a piece of styrofoam is a completely inadequate substitute for looking or feeling for oneself. There are, however, the questions of how much guidance the teacher should provide for the children as they manipulate and observe and how much discussion and review should follow the experience. How much verbalization should take place?

It is our belief that there should be substantial guidance and discussion. There should be an effort to relate the unusual experience which represents an extreme case to the more usual experience. The description of the current teaching program in Chapter III will illustrate how this can be accomplished. In this way, the abstract

Observing the behavior of snails

concepts that are at the basis of the scientific point of view are built up. As the children make further observations, they will look at them more scientifically. The abstractions will form a link between their earlier experiences and later experiences so that the children can bring their knowledge to bear in a systematic way. Perhaps the gulf between scientific thinking and common-sense thinking can be reduced.

Each lesson in the science program may fulfill one or both of these two functions: to provide a new experience and to establish or reinforce an abstract concept. Connections between different lessons are created by use of the same phenomenon to illustrate different concepts and the use of the same concept to interpret different phenomena. The conceptual structure creates a context for the new experience that enables it to be assimilated rationally in relation to other experiences. One might say that the structure provides discipline for mental organization. In the end, the student will not only be able to conduct experiments and understand scientific explanations—he will also have the intellectual tools to review and analyze his own procedures and reasoning.

III

The SCIS Program—A Current Look

SCOPE AND SEQUENCE OF THE CURRICULUM

On the basis of the theoretical considerations of Chapter II, one may try to construct a curriculum plan that assures a sound connection between the children's intuitive approach and the concepts of the modern scientific point of view. Such a plan is a guide for the development of individual teaching units. It must be regarded as tentative, however, until the curriculum is completed, because the trial teaching experience will in all likelihood compel reconsideration and revision. Figure 1 displays the overall plan of the SCIS curriculum as presently envisaged. Some of the units are currently available, while others (identified with a question mark) are still in the planning stage.

Progression in the sequence takes place from the top to the bottom of the chart. Each major concept of study is indicated by a box. The lines connecting the boxes represent the interdependence of the concepts. Four successive levels of abstraction are indicated because they roughly relate the sequence to the stages in child development. Level I corresponds to the transition from pre-operational to concrete operational thought. Level II is adapted to the concrete operational stage. Level III corresponds to the transition between concrete operational thought and the stage of formal operations. Level IV, finally, requires considerable facility with formal operations. These divisions, however are not clear-cut, and they cannot be taken as rigid guideposts.

It can be seen that the introductory work of Level I divides into three loosely related strands on Level II. These are the physical

FIGURE 1 Science Curriculum Improvement Study

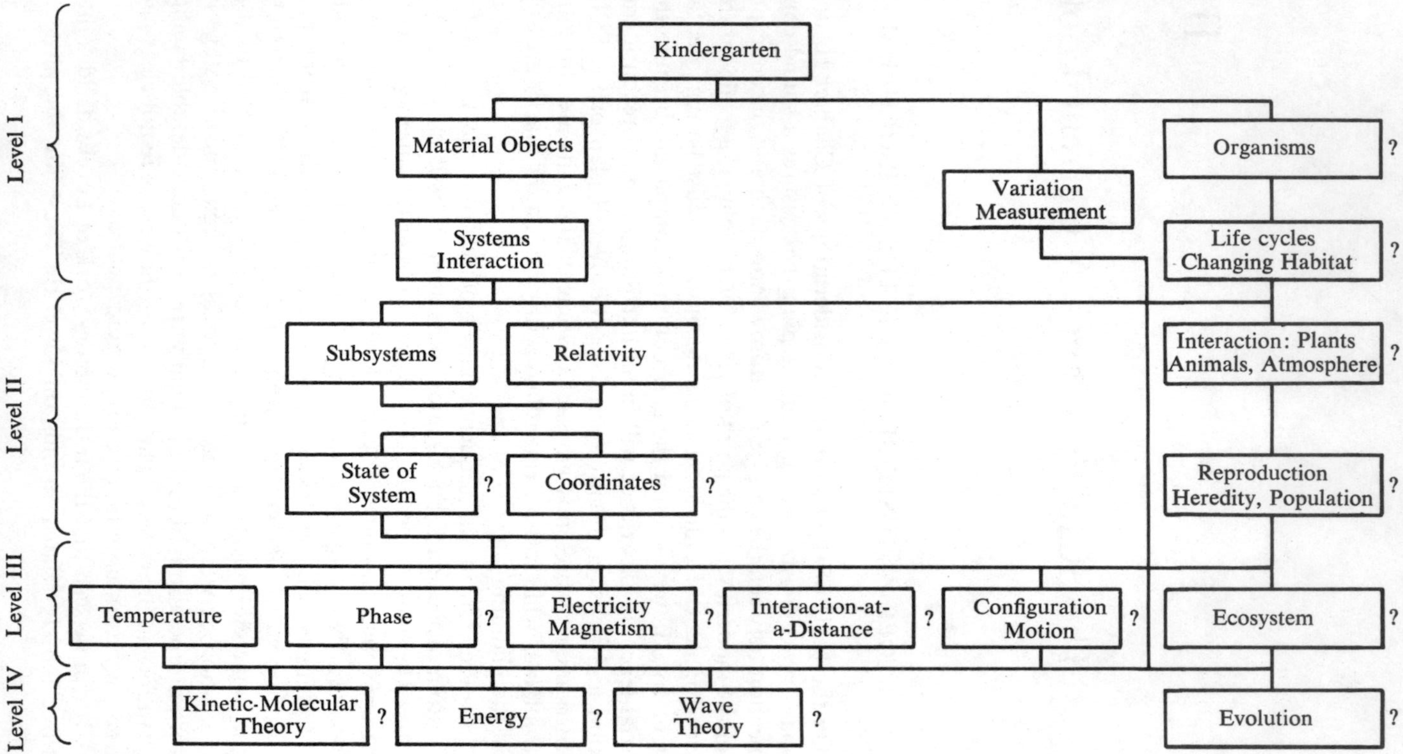

sciences, the life sciences, and quantitative comparisons. On Level III, the quantitative treatment is integrated into the other two to make possible experimental investigation of the inter-dependence of the variables, such as time, temperature, and rates of change, that are used to describe phenomena in physical and biological systems. The interrelation of physical and life sciences will become evident through a study of the effect of physical factors in living organisms in the experimental work on Level III and through a study of energy and energy transfer on Level IV. The development of the life science program is under the direction of Chester Lawson, Professor of Natural Science at Michigan State University. The upper grade physical sciences units are being prepared under the leadership of Luke E. Steiner, until recently Professor of Chemistry at Oberlin College, and Robert Karplus.

The remaining sections of this chapter will elucidate the general pattern of the teaching units and the details of some of the units that exist at present. It will be valuable for the reader to refer to Figure 1 occasionally as he continues with this chapter.

PLAN OF A TEACHING UNIT

Each SCIS teaching unit is arranged according to a teaching strategy aimed at the twofold objectives of providing new experiences and establishing one or more abstract concepts. At the core of the unit is the definition of the abstraction either through concrete instances or through concrete operations.

Prior to the introduction of the definition, there is an instructional period of several class sessions in which the children engage in exploratory experimentation with some new and some familiar materials. At this time they review and deepen their understanding of previously formed concepts, but they are also faced with some problems with which they cannot yet deal adequately. During these sessions the teacher may appraise the children's comprehension, skills, and attitudes as developed by the preceding units.

In *Interaction*, for example, children can observe the color change when vinegar acts on blue litmus paper, and they can observe the heating when a wire is used to short-circuit a dry cell. Both of these changes are mysterious for most children because they have never encountered something similar. At a later stage they will become familiar with the circumstances under which such changes occur. For the present, the children's work arouses interest, and their descriptions of their observations enable the teacher to determine whether they can identify a system for an experiment and whether they have the manipulative skill to handle the equipment successfully.

After the children have become familiar with the new materials, the teacher introduces the key concept to lead the children to a new way of thinking about their experiences. The concept is defined as concretely as possible with the help of experimental demonstrations text material, and audio-visual aids. It is important that the teacher explain the definition clearly. While he should not attempt to achieve a consensus about the content of the definition, he must permit the children to review and discuss the validity of its applications.

The name of the concept is also provided because children grasp a stable and usable concept more easily when they have a verbal label which helps them communicate with themselves and with others. For instance, the concept of material is introduced by the teacher after the children have sorted a set of pieces of brass, aluminum, pine, walnut, and vinyl plastic in the unit *Material Objects*. This concept enables them to explain a new way of sorting the set; it extends their previously developed ability to group objects according to size, color, shape, and texture. Another example is the concept of relative position of a system as defined by its distance in a certain direction from an observer. This concept is introduced in the *Relativity* unit.

The remaining part of each of the units is largely devoted to experimentation and explanation by the children as they test the consequences of using the new concept. This work gives them opportunities to apply their understanding to many examples. It also affords the teacher chances to observe the children's work and, if necessary, to review the definition. For these activities to have the desired educational value and to serve the evaluation function, it is important that the teacher encourage the children without prescribing their observations and explanations in detail. These must be developed at the children's own initiative, with the children free to learn from their experience and from one another even by making mistakes and drawing invalid conclusions.

Above and beyond these aspects, however, the remainder of the

Children sort by material, using pieces of metal

unit involves the children in exciting exploration of new phenomena and new problems. Here they can try out their ideas, gain experience with the conditions under which something will or will not happen, make hypotheses about the outcomes of experiments, evaluate evidence, draw conclusions from their observations, discuss their results with other children, and otherwise engage in the processes of science. Appropriately, the bulk of the teaching time in a unit is devoted to this kind of activity. The ingenuity of the children and of the teacher can lead the class to imaginative uses of the equipment provided or of equipment they improvise to expand the suggested procedures as they desire.

In *Variation and Measurement*, for example, the histogram, a graphical way to describe a set of observations, is used to show the distribution of family sizes of the children in a class. In *Subsystems*, the children observe liquid Freon first vaporize and inflate a plastic bag, then liquefy when cooled with ice cubes. The significant

A second grader studies the variation in the number of peas in a pod

changes that occur in this experiment are attributed to properties of the Freon subsystem and are not specific to the other interacting objects such as the containers, the ice cubes, and so on. In *Interaction*, the children seek evidence of interaction between a dry cell and a motor, a light bulb, and other components.

To contrast those lessons in which a new concept is introduced with those in which a concept is applied to new experiences, we use the words *invention* and *discovery*. In our meaning, a conceptual invention is a new idea for interpreting experience, an idea which resulted from an inductive mental leap. A discovery is the recognition of a relationship between an idea and an observation, or between two ideas, or between two observations. A lesson in which a new concept is introduced may therefore be called an invention lesson, while the application of the concept gives rise to discovery lessons. The plan of a unit may be seen, therefore, to consist of this sequence: preliminary exploration, invention, and discovery. Most of the teaching time is devoted to discovery lessons, but the other two parts are essential.

Is there evidence of interaction?

The distinction between invention and discovery has been very useful in the construction of new units because it pinpoints the fact that some things can be discovered but others cannot. The latter are the man-made concepts, such as color, size, material, system, interaction, position, and energy, in terms of which scientists think about natural phenomena. The former are the outcomes of specific experiments or observations such as the color of a piece of brass, the materials of the parts of a pencil, the ability of certain objects to interact with a compass needle, and so on.

To make discoveries, however, the observer has to have certain concepts clearly in mind. In the construction of a unit, therefore, the authors have to decide what mental operations, what discoveries, should be triggered by the children's experimental work. They must then plan the unit so that the necessary concepts are either available from previous units or are "invented" in earlier parts of the unit under consideration. Thus, the children who experiment with thermometer stems and ice cubes in the *Interaction* unit have been introduced to the systems concept in the *Systems* unit and to the interaction concept in the *Interaction* unit; they are therefore able to define the ice-cube-and-thermometer-stem system and to recognize that the falling of the liquid is evidence of its interaction with the ice cube. These considerations guide the decisions of sequence and structure of the entire curriculum (see Figure 1) and of sequence within a unit. The latter will be represented in small charts in the following sections of this chapter.

It is sometimes convenient to group closely-related concepts together into one unit so as to obtain a teaching sequence of convenient and manageable duration. In that case, there may be several "invention" lessons, each preceded by introductory or problem-raising activities and each followed by discovery experiences in which the new concept may be applied repeatedly at the pupils' initiative. The *Material Objects* unit, for example, includes the "invention" of the concepts of object, property, material, and serial ordering. Other concepts, such as color, shape, and texture, are not "invented" in *Material Objects* but are assumed to be understood by the children as a result of the kindergarten program. If this assumption is unjustified, the teacher has to take remedial steps. Still other concepts, such as system and interaction, are foreshadowed in experiments the children carry out during their work with *Material Objects* but are "invented" and made part of the pupils' vocabulary only in later units.

SCOPE AND SEQUENCE OF THE MATERIAL OBJECTS UNIT

The main objective of the unit is to familiarize children with some of the material objects (pieces of matter) in their environment. The range of objects chosen is as broad as is conveniently possible. Ultimately, the word *object* is given a meaning beyond the conventional one. Samples of liquid and even samples of gas are identified as objects because they are material in nature.

The reader may like to consider, for contrast, what would not be regarded as an object in this sense. All abstractions, such as love and hate, time and space, beauty and color, hunger and thirst, and so on, are examples of things that are not material objects. The word *thing*, which can be used to refer to abstractions, has too broad a meaning to be useful in a science program which tries to communicate a concept of matter. For the children, the contrast

Experimenting with air

between objects and "nonobjects" is made in later units; for the present, they become acquainted with the objects in their environment and merely distinguish them from their properties.

The unit has a fairly complex plan in which the cycle of preliminary explorations, invention, and discovery occurs three times. Figure 2 summarizes the unit's plan and also shows how the activities in the last two chapters foreshadow the work of subsequent units.

The first chapter bases the introduction of the concepts *object* and *property* on familiar objects of the classroom, home, and playground. The new ideas are applied to other objects, to plants and animals and their parts, and to collections of buttons and wooden blocks that can be sorted according to a number of properties such as shape, color, texture, size, and so on.

In Chapter II, the children's comparison of similarly shaped pieces of aluminum, brass, pine, walnut, plexiglass, and polystyrene leads to the introduction of the concept of material. This idea is then applied in additional work with other metals, various kinds of wood, rocks, liquids, and gases.

FIGURE 2 Plan of the Material Objects Unit

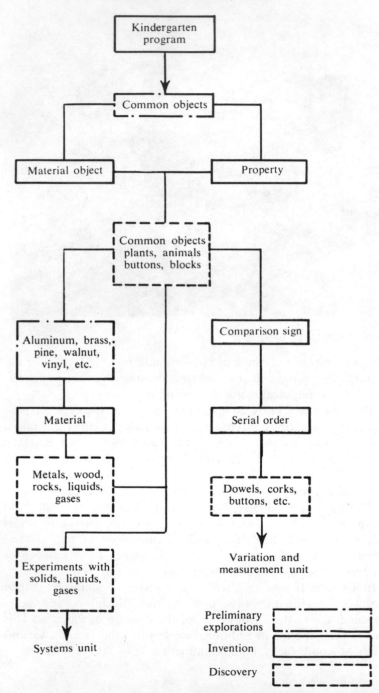

In Chapter III, the comparison sign ($\rangle$ or $\langle$) and serial ordering are introduced to give a semiquantitative aspect to the children's comparison of objects. Chapter IV, finally, allows the children to carry out experiments in which they collect evidence of what material lump sugar and rock candy are composed of, test whether

Does it float or sink? A first grader studies objects

objects float or sink in water, and use air to displace water from submerged containers. These experiments give the children opportunities to apply what they have learned of material objects and their properties.

SCOPE AND SEQUENCE OF THE SYSTEMS UNIT

The word *system* is being used more and more frequently. Communication systems, electronic systems, and systems analysis are discussed in newspapers, in magazines, and on television. In all these discussions, and in this unit as well, the word *system* refers to objects that are being mentally separated from everything else to receive special attention. A system is a group of objects that is treated as a unit.

Of course, there have to be reasons why a certain system of objects receives special attention. It may be that the objects can be combined to form a pattern, like pieces of tile in a mosaic. It may be that the objects can be combined to trigger a process of change, as when a match is struck on sandpaper. In either example, the system of objects is a whole which has properties not possessed by the individual objects. This is the crux of the systems concept.

In a way, everyone uses the systems concept informally without even being aware of it. One focusses his attention temporarily on parts of his environment and ignores or neglects other parts because the totality of impressions reaching him at the moment is too complex and confusing to be grasped at once. The teacher can make good use of the systems concept to help him communicate with his pupils. He may use it to focus the children's attention on a magnet and a nail, on a sample of liquid, on a piece of apparatus, or on only a part of a piece of apparatus. He may also use it to learn what has attracted the children's attention or what they judge to be important. He does this by asking them to tell what objects they chose for their system.

Preliminary explorations, invention, and discovery are the three steps in the teaching of the systems concept in the unit. Figure 3 shows the plan of the unit, including its relation to preceding units and to units that follow in the curriculum.

The first chapter provides activities that prepare for the introduction of the systems concept. In this chapter, the children engage in two activities to construct a whole that is made up of parts—an experimental set-up and a pattern of blocks. In Chapter II the word *system* is introduced to refer to a whole that is made up of parts (*invention*). The remaining chapters give the children opportunities for *discovery*—that is, for applying the new concept in experimental situations of their own making (Chapter III), to phenomena in their environment (Chaper IV), and to pictorial representations of phenomena (Chapter V). They also give the teacher opportunities to introduce ways of representing systems in illustrations. Even at the conclusion of the unit, the children's

FIGURE 3 Plan of the Systems Unit

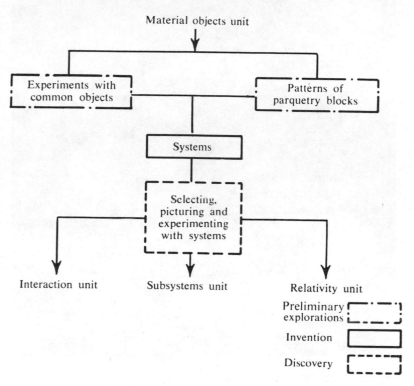

understanding of systems is incomplete; it is increased as they progress through subsequent SCIS units. The systems concept is a thread that weaves throughout the science program.

As was pointed out on page 17, the *Systems* unit in its present form proved too abstract and time consuming in relation to its educational value. The current plan, therefore, is to incorporate some of the preliminary activities and the invention of the system concept into the *Interaction* unit (see below) and to eliminate *Systems* as a separate unit.

SCOPE AND SEQUENCE OF THE INTERACTION UNIT

The interaction concept is being used more and more to explain social and scientific phenomena. At conferences one may find

Investigating systems of liquids

strong interaction among some participants, but weak interaction among others; erosion is caused by the interaction of wind and water with rock; in the laboratory, magnets interact even when they are not touching. In ancient times some philosophers took the view that changes were brought about by an ultimate fate or destiny that was inherent in every object. Now we say that a change is brought about by interaction, and we try to determine the conditions under which the interaction occurs.

Finding regular patterns of behavior is the goal of the scientist who examines natural phenomena. When he finds regularity, he gains some confidence about his ability to predict the outcome of certain experiments because he expects them to fit the same pattern. In this way the scientist is not very different from the rest of us. All of us are uncomfortable in a completely new situation. All of us, from childhood on, accumulate through experience knowledge about what is likely to happen in many circumstances. This gives us confidence in facing the future because we have a pretty good idea of what will happen next.

One of the most important kinds of patterns is the one that leads to cause-and-effect interpretations. If a scientist observes a certain change which always follows when some objects are near each other and which never occurs otherwise, he will hypothesize that the objects are interacting and have a cause-and-effect relationship. The scientist and the layman infer the existence of interaction from observable evidence, from changes that occur in the persons or the objects involved in a phenomenon. Interpreting changes in terms of interaction appears to satisfy a psychological need for explaining observations.

An aim of this unit is to help children recognize regular patterns of behavior. The first step is to identify the system of material objects that is present and seems to be connected with a happening. The second step is to recognize that changes are taking place during the period of observation—changes in shape, position, color, temperature, appearance, or other details. The third step is to determine which object or objects were instrumental in causing the change. This step is the one that leads to the interaction concept. Therefore, observation of change is evidence of interaction. The statement that objects interact is merely a statement that they affect or change each other.

Preliminary explorations, invention, and discovery are used in the unit to teach the interaction concept and interaction-at-a-distance. Figure 4 shows the plan of the unit, which is somewhat more complicated than *Systems*. The relation to the *Systems* unit and to more advanced units of the science program is also indicated.

The first chapter provides activities in which the children bring about and observe changes in order to prepare for the introduction of the interaction concept. In Chapter II the teacher then introduces the word *interact* to express the relation of objects that exert a mutual influence on one another (*invention*). In Chapter III the teacher and the pupils consider once again the changes they observe, but now these changes may be interpreted as evidence of interaction. The remaining chapters give the children opportunities for *discovery*—that is, for applying the new concept to experiments on the dissolving of copper chloride, the reaction of copper chloride with aluminum, and the reaction of breath with

FIGURE 4 Plan of the Interaction Unit

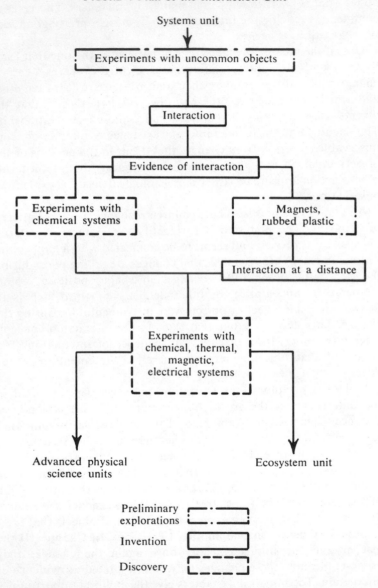

bromothymol blue (Chapter IV); to objects that interact without touching (Chapter V); to slow chemical changes (Chapter VI); and to temperature changes, magnets, and electrical circuits (Chapter

VII). During their activities, the children make reports of their observations in terms of the system for an experiment and the evidence of interaction. In Chapter Five, an additional concept is introduced, the concept of *interaction-at-a-distance*.

Finding evidence of interaction between dry cells and light bulbs

The exploring activities in the first chapter lead the children to consider the changes that are observed. A change may occur in the properties of the objects involved, such as when vinegar turns blue litmus red, or in their arrangement relative to each other. Sometimes a change is observed in only one object in a system. The scientist however, believes that some changes are taking place in other objects in that same system, even though these may be hard to observe. When scissors and paper interact, for example, one observed change is in the shape of the paper. Actually the edges of the blades of the scissors are becoming slightly dull, but this is difficult to observe. Another change, the motion of the blades of the scissors, is due to the interaction of the scissors with the hand.

The invention lessons in the second and third chapters introduce the conceptual steps whose accomplishment is the principal objective of the entire unit. The teacher explains that he will use the word *interaction* to refer to the relationship of objects that are affecting one another and that the observable change or changes which show the effect are *evidence of interaction*.

The discovery lessons in the remainder of the unit allow children to make many applications of the interaction concept so as to reinforce and broaden its meaning for them. In a variety of

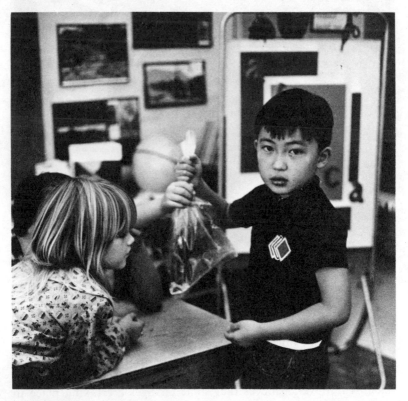

Investigating Freon: a study of a subsystem

experiments, they observe different kinds of changes—dissolving, bubbling, color changing, thermal expansion, moving, heating, and many others. They also have the opportunities to compare pictures of systems and verbal records of their observations.

Note that the original objects which interact do not survive in recognizable form in all of the processes, such as in the interaction of aluminum foil with a copper chloride solution in Chapter IV. In a change such as this, a satisfactory explanation is possible only through the recognition that atomic and molecular rearrangements are taking place. From the children's point of view, however, such an explanation is meaningless; they have to be content with describing the changes that they can observe and interpreting these as evidence of interaction.

SCOPE AND THE SEQUENCE OF THE SUBSYSTEMS UNIT

The concept of subsystem is an extension of the systems concept. Sometimes one deals with the system for an experiment but attention is really focused on only part of the system—consider, for instance, a cup containing some water, an ice cube, and a thermometer. One may concentrate on individual parts of that experimental system such as the ice, the ice and water, the thermometer, or even the cup itself. These interesting parts, then, become systems to the observer as he focuses attention on each one or their various combinations in turn. Since each of these systems is wholly contained within the original system, it is called a *sub*system. The alternate or concurrent use of a system and of one or more subsystems gives the scientist great flexibility in applying the systems concept to an entire complex phenomenon and yet attending to fine details. Other examples of subsystems within experimental systems are the dry cell in an electrical circuit or the glowing light bulb in the same circuit. The fact that the dry cell contains chemicals which are interacting to produce an electric current makes this subsystem selection useful.

The subsystems concept is introduced in the SCIS curriculum for a definite reason. As children become more aware of the complexity of phenomena in their environment, they find their attention drawn simultaneously to different groups of objects. The subsystems concept enables them to deal with this problem by first choosing a fairly comprehensive system that includes all participating objects, but then concentrating on one or more subsystems which can be studied in detail.

The following example illustrates the flexibility inherent in the system-subsystem relationship. Consider a railroad train, say on the Southern Pacific Railroad. This can be regarded as a system composed of an engine and several cars. Now, it is possible to examine any one of these objects as being itself a system—a subsystem of the train—composed of objects such as the body, roof, wheels, wheel trucks, and so on. Each of these, in turn, can be considered as a system—a "sub-subsystem" of the train—composed of objects, e.g., the wheel having a disk, a rim, a bearing, etc. In this way, objects in a system are themselves considered systems made up of still smaller objects until one arrives at molecular, atomic, and subatomic systems.

One can also progress in the opposite direction to larger and more comprehensive structures. The one railroad train is then only a subsystem of the entire Southern Pacific Railroad system which includes other trains, tracks, stations, real estate, and so on. The Southern Pacific, in turn, is a subsystem of the nationwide railroad network which is itself a subsystem of the entire transportation system consisting of railroads, airlines, truck lines, bus lines, barge canals, taxicabs, etc.

As was the case with the units discussed previously, preliminary explorations, invention, and discovery are used to teach the subsystems concept. By the choice of activities, however, the unit also foreshadows some of the phenomena children will encounter in more advanced physical science units. The plan of the unit is shown in Figure 5.

The first chapter provides activities that prepare for the introduction of the subsystems concept. In this chapter the children experiment with six different liquids and then with mixtures of solid materials and water. In both instances there are parts of the entire experimental set-up which are themselves composed of parts such as the liquids (composed of drops) and the solids (composed of granules). In Chapter II the word *subsystem* is introduced to refer to parts of a system which are themselves a system (*invention*). The remaining chapters give the children opportunities for *discovery*, that is, for applying the new concept to experiments with an electromagnet (Chapter III), to vaporization and condensation phenomena (Chapter IV), to solutions of salt and water (Chapter V), and to mixtures of liquids and water (Chapter VI). During their activities, the children gain experience in comparing their observations with pictorial representations of the same phenomena, in adducing evidence to support their hypotheses, in making simple records of their observations, and in using a powerful magnifier as a tool.

FIGURE 5 Plan of the Subsystems Unit

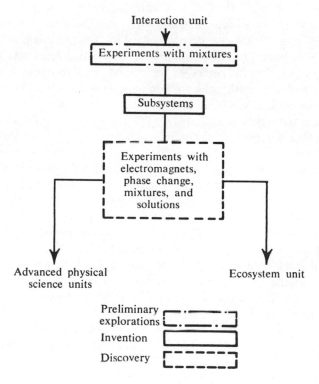

The concept of subsystems has a natural employment in these activities, which involve somewhat more complex phenomena than the children have encountered previously. Instead of using a permanent magnet that is provided by the teacher, for example, they construct an electromagnet out of a coil of wire and a bolt. Such an electromagnet is clearly a system—a whole composed of parts—yet it also is a subsystem when one thinks of it in a larger system along with objects such as a dry cell and some paper clips. Similar considerations apply to the mixtures of the various solid and liquid materials. Each of the materials is a system made up of granules or drops, but each is also a subsystem when combined with other materials in the mixture and a container.

SCOPE AND SEQUENCE OF THE RELATIVITY UNIT

The word RELATIVITY is usually associated with mathematical mystery and scientific complexity, yet the basic concept is simple. The matters of concern in relativity are the position and motion of objects. The basic concept is that position and motion of an object can only be perceived, described, and recognized with reference to other nearby objects. These other objects, to which the position or motion are related, are said to form a REFERENCE FRAME, and one speaks of POSITION or MOTION of the original object relative to the reference frame.

How could a proofreader, for instance, describe the position of an erroneous comma on this page of the book? Most directly, he could point to it with his finger or circle it with his pencil. These actions would indicate the position in a direct and non-verbal way to someone else who looks at the same copy of the page. To communicate the position of the comma to someone who does not have access to the same copy of the page is much more difficult. One could then try to relate it to the four edges of the paper, to the structure of the text in terms of paragraphs, and to the adjacent words in the text. These elements of the printed page are thus used as reference frame.

For practical purposes, the objects making up the reference frame must be easily located and identified. Otherwise they cannot be used as guides to assist in finding the object whose position is being described. It would be difficult, for example, to try to find the comma on the printed page if its position were described by saying, "The comma is near a letter '*e*'." Something more distinctive is needed, as was indicated above.

Our everyday techniques for describing position of an object make use of the many objects in our environment together with qualitative descriptions of distances and directions such as "near to," "far from," "almost directly to the left," or "slightly east of north." In some situations, however, as for a ship at sea, a caravan in the desert, an eskimo in an ice field, or an astronaut in space, there may be no distinctive nearby objects at all relative to which position may be identified. In such a case it is necessary to construct a reference frame using remote objects with an ensuing need for precise measurements. One such reference frame is provided by the earth itself through its equator, the poles, and the measurement of latitude and longitude. For the space traveller, a reference frame based on the stars will have to be created.

So far we have described so-called environmental reference frames, which are derived from objects in the near or remote environment. It is often convenient to use one's body as a reference frame, such as when one describes another object as being in front, or to the right. The personal reference frame becomes very helpful when one is in a ship at sea, where the bow, stern, port, and starboard directions are in common use. The astronaut in a space ship engaged in a rendez-vous maneuver has a still more difficult problem, because for him the up and down directions, usually identified by the effects of earth's gravity, are no longer recognizable. He has only his personal reference directions to rely upon.

The laboratory scientist, who tries to describe natural phenomena in a very general way, avoids using incidental reference objects, such as laboratory walls or table surfaces, as reference frames. He tries to include in his description only those objects that are interacting in a significant way with the experimental system. To avoid bias, he frequently uses a completely artificial reference frame consisting of arbitrarily chosen reference points and reference directions. This is a highly abstract procedure. To make it somewhat more concrete, it is helpful to invent an artificial observer who is placed so that the scientist's reference frame is his personal reference frame. This observer has no function other than to represent the reference point by his body and to represent the reference direction by the way he is facing.

So far we have considered ways of describing the relative position of objects which are stationary. Now let us consider objects which change their position with time. When an object changes position, we commonly say that it "moved," that it is "in motion." But what do we mean by motion? Since position depends on the reference frame, it is plausible to expect that motion also depends on the reference frame. It is therefore customary to use the phrase "relative motion."

Imagine that a truck is being described relative to two different reference frames. Reference frame A is attached to the roadway, reference frame B to the truck. To make the description simpler and more concrete, we shall introduce two artificial observers, one representing each reference frame.

As the truck drives down the road, Observer A reports its position first on his left, then in front of him, then on his right. The position of the truck relative to Observer A has changed over time. But Observer B always reports the truck as being in the same position, with the platform under his feet and the driver's cab on his left. The position of the truck relative to Observer B, therefore, did not change from the beginning to the end of the experiment. Thus, we find that we have two different sets of data, one from each reference frame. In one reference frame we would conclude that the position has changed and in the other the position has not changed. If we define relative motion as the change of position relative to a reference frame, then the two observers disagree not only about the relative position of the truck at various times in the experiment but they will also disagree about the truck's relative motion.

We can extend the discussion to motion of other objects. For instance, does the earth move? This depends on the reference frame we use to define the earth's position. Relative to the earth-fixed reference frame, to which we are most accustomed, the earth is stationary. Relative to a sun-fixed reference frame, however, the earth moves in its orbit.

In order to determine the position and motion of objects in an experiment, it is important to decide upon a reference frame. It is especially important when change in position is going to be interpreted as evidence of interaction. Depending on the, frame of reference, an observer may or may not find evidence of interaction.

Let us briefly look at some of the consequences of our concept of relative motion, consequences which may seem either fascinating or merely strange, depending on how willing we are to break out of habitual modes of thinking. Already we have noted that observers may disagree about the relative motion of an object. We must also require that our artificial observer report an object to be stationary in his reference frame so long as he is attached to that object. Such an observer's report about the rest of the world will seem unusual indeed, if the observer's reference frame is attached to a merry-go-round, a satellite in orbit, or a sewing machine needle.

Another consequence of the relative motion concept is that different observers might disagree about the direction and the speed of an object they both observe. Think about this example, in which an object travels at different speeds relative to different reference frames.

The speed of a river boat going upstream as reported by its passengers looking at the shore line is a snail-like 1 mph, but the speed as reported by the captain is a respectable 10 mph. Who is right? The objective of the passengers may be to reach a certain destination on shore, yet all navigation and propulsion takes place in the reference frame of the water. Unless the water is still, the motion of a river boat relative to the shore is different from its motion relative to the water. Since the water is flowing downstream at a speed of 9 mph (relative to the shore), and the river boat is traveling upstream at a speed of 10 mph (relative to the water), the speed of the river boat (relative to the shore) is 1 mph. Thus, the conflicting reports of the two observers are understandable and correct, for they are observing from different reference frames. The question, "Who is right?," can only be answered, "Both are right."

The Relativity unit is divided into two major parts. Part I builds the concept of relative position on some of the children's intuitive notions of distance and direction. The activities, therefore, begin with the qualitative description of the placement of objects in the child's environment and end with the use of polar coordinates for the precise location of objects relative to a reference frame.

Like *system* and *interaction, reference frame* is a conceptual invention. Objects in our environment have the potential to be reference frames, but they actually become reference frames only when someone decides to use them for describing the relative position or the relative motion of other objects. The teaching program of the Relativity unit therefore aims at the two-fold objective of giving children the ability to use reference frames and the initiative to select reference frames when that is necessary.

The central idea of the unit is the necessity of describing position relative to a reference frame. This idea is introduced to the children in Chapter III. Prior to this, the children use reference frames, such as large objects in their surroundings (Chapter I), the figure of an artificial observer, Mr. O (Chapter II), and landmarks in their community and a playground model (Chapter III), so as to become gradually aware of this process. In Chapter IV the children learn about the use of coordinates to describe relative position numerically. This chapter contains many applications of the reference frame idea to describe position, to locate objects, and to give the children practice in using protractors, rulers, and coordinate grids as tools for determining relative position.

In planning Part II, two possible approaches were considered. One was to proceed logically from the concept of relative position to comparison and change of relative position, and from change of relative position to relative motion. The other approach was to begin with activities that emphasize the smoothness and continuity of motion, for which children have an intuitive grasp. After this start, the children would be led to recognize the many successive positions that were taken up by a moving object and the changes in position that occurred between.

We chose the second approach, because it promised to create a better link between the children's preconceptions and modern science than did the logical approach. One must also remember that the logical reasoning ability of nine-to-ten-year-old children is limited.

The beginning of Part II, therefore, does not make direct reference to the question of relative position. Instead, it concentrates on moving objects (a pen making patterns on a piece of paper, a story of a boy in the forest, a film of orbiting astronauts), but it does raise questions about the possibility of disagreement among different observers of the motion. These explorations set the stage for the invention lesson in Chapter VI. After the invention lesson, some of the children's experiences with moving objects are examined in a more analytical way. Once the notion of position is connected with motion, the reference frame for describing position also becomes an important consideration in describing motion. The unit concludes with a discussion of the films seen earlier and with the making of flip books, in which the children can express their own ideas of objects in motion.

A schematic outline of RELATIVITY is presented in Figure 6, which shows the interrelationship of the preliminary exploration, invention, and discovery activities mentioned above. Also to be noted are that the ideas of this unit contribute to the state of a system concept and to the use of coordinates for a quantitative numerical description of relative positions in more advanced physical science units.

One key tool in the development of the reference frame idea is

Figure 6 Plan of the Relativity Unit

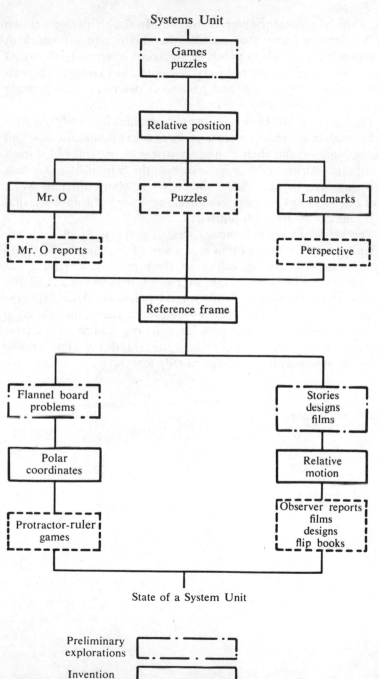

the artificial egocentric observer, Mr. O. Mr. O is the personification of a reference frame that enables the children to grapple with apparently contradictory points of view on a concrete level. Mr. O directs his attention at the objects we choose, he "knows" where all these objects are located, and he always describes their position relative to his own person.

The fact that Mr. O is egocentric, somewhat like children tend to be, enables the children more easily to take his point of view and thereby to overcome their own egocentric outlook. One of the most significant insights children achieve with the help of Mr. O is that situations can be described "correctly" in many different ways, that one right answer does not preclude other right answers, that everyone can be right for himself.

The children's science experiences in previous SCIS units are extended by RELATIVITY in many ways. For example, flexibility in grouping objects according to their properties, which was introduced in MATERIAL OBJECTS, is broadened to a flexibility in describing phenomena from several points of view. Also, the selection of a system of objects as focus of attention introduced in SYSTEMS is made sharper as children are required to make a clear separation between an object or system and the conventional reference frame with which it is usually associated.

IV

The Role and Involvement of
The Learner in The Science Program

INTRODUCTION

Take a walk around the school and collect objects. Count the number of peas in each of a population of pea pods. Have a punch party. Put some vinegar into a jar of bromothymol blue and water. Mix some table salt with water. Observe the change in temperature of a jar of hot water standing in the classroom. Can these be examples of a present-day revolution in our elementary school science teaching? Should not the "new curriculum" concern itself with space satellites or traveling to the moon? Perhaps while reading the first three chapters in this book you were asking yourself similar questions. The answers are not simple; they involve considerations of what is basic to the structure of science, as well as what is known about the ways on which young children learn.

The relationship of the structure of science to the development of the Science Curriculum Improvement Study has been developed in Chapters II and III. In this chapter, a closer look will be taken at the role and involvement of the pupil in the science program. These considerations are an integral part of the core of ideas forming the basis for the development of the program of the Science Curriculum Improvement Study.

It is true that the present accomplishment and future plans of man's exploration of space are exciting and of some interest to young children, but, considering the experience and level of understanding of the young child (or even of most adults), is there very much science involved? Probably not. Where the satellite travels, from where it leaves, who is inside—these are all interesting facts, but they are more closely related to current events or social studies for the elementary school pupil. The young child can talk about them, but his ability to have an immediate, direct personal experience with the problem of satellite travel is nonexistent.

It is true that the space scientists are concerned with problems such as the rate of temperature rise and fall in the cabin during re-entry. They are also interested in the rate at which solids, liquids, and gases dissolve into each other and come out of solution at various temperatures and pressures. Painstaking observation of the evidence of interaction between test satellites and the atmosphere is vital for making decisions as to whether or not a vehicle is ready for manned flight. Although the careful counting of the number of peas in a pod is not a significant problem for the space scientist, an understanding of probability (which can be introduced with the pea pods) is most important when one is trying to predict the possibilities of achieving a given orbit. In other words, the kinds of *direct experience* provided by the activities described as a part of the Science Curriculum Improvement Study involve the pupil with concepts basic to the structure of science.

For some children (a small percentage) this will be the introduction to what will become a professional interest and perhaps even the development of the knowledge and ability to make a contribution in the complex technology or science of space travel. For the most part, however, we are interested in developing an educated layman who is capable of living productively in a society where science is and will be playing an important role. We want the youngster to understand not only the basic structure but also the rationale and way of thinking that characterize modern-day science. Not only should he be aware of and appreciate the accomplishments of, but he also needs to realize the limitations of, science and scientists, especially when applied to problems which do not lend themselves to scientific analysis at the present time.

How young children learn science, or anything else for that matter, is an interesting and provocative question. The course of a child's intellectual development during ages six to fourteen changes greatly. The child's thinking undergoes a gradual transition from concrete to abstract. In order to help him achieve this, the elementary science program must provide the individual child with many concrete experiences in manipulating objects and systems in the environment. At the beginning of this period the child is achieving mastery of his muscles and gaining the ability to carry out physical manipulations; in his thinking he is dependent on direct experience. At the end the child is achieving a degree of mastery of mind; he is able to focus his thoughts consciously and to manipulate abstract relationships without constant reference to specific examples.

DEGREE OF INVOLVEMENT

While considering this need, let us look at some of the degrees of involvement which the child can have in the science program. The minimal amount takes place when he reads a book about science. It is verbal and abstract. The child's possible level of understanding is controlled not only by his comprehension of the printed word, but also by the author's ability to use language to describe his subjects clearly. These restrictions place severe limitations on the young child's participation in the science program. Even if he is able to read and repeat the words of science, no information is available as to whether the child has had experience with or understands the phenomena involved. In addition, the opportunities for pupil–pupil interaction based on common experience are non-existent. This pupil–pupil interaction, which occurs when children have common experiences and can discuss them among themselves, is most important in the children's intellectual development. Justifying a position or disagreeing with one's peers causes the individual to reconsider and re-evaluate his own decisions. But without pupil–pupil interaction, the program for the children becomes one of reading about rather than experiencing science.

A somewhat higher degree of involvement takes place when the child participates in a classroom discussion about science readings. The discussion, although limited to verbal descriptions about science, does have the added advantage of the give-and-take between pupil and teacher or pupil and pupil. Through this give-and-take, the child hears modifications and explanations of the verbal description and is somewhat more actively involved. He can ask questions, the answers to which may lead to greater understanding. It should be realized, however, that the answers may also tend to confuse the child since the entire operation is usually on the verbal-abstract level. There is no commonality of actual experience and therefore little possibility of a real discussion. Frequently the so-called discussion is completely teacher-dominated and actually is the teacher asking questions and fishing for pre-determined answers. This is not a discussion of science (since no science has taken place for the discussants) but rather is a talk about science as presented in a given textbook or other source.

A third and still higher degree of involvement for the child takes place when a demonstration using systems of objects to illustrate some natural phenomena is carried out in the class. Whether the

Involving children in science

teacher or a small group of children execute the demonstration is of little importance in the context of this discussion. The involvement of the teacher or children doing the demonstration will be greater than that of the watchers. If we are thinking of the participation of each child in the class in the science program, then the technique of having a child demonstrate does not make much difference. Sometimes the child's lack of awareness of problems of visibility and technique makes this approach to classroom demonstrations less valuable than having the teacher demonstrate. It is assumed that the teacher will be sensitive to these problems of technique and visibility.

Finally, there comes the fourth and highest degree of involvement of the child in the science program. At this level the individual child is confronted by the systems of objects he chooses or which are chosen from the environment, and he watches the objects and

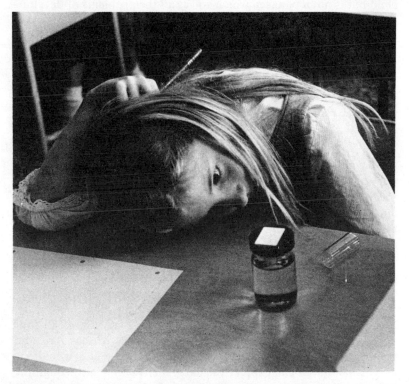

Observing the properties of a solution

what happens to them. The observations are individual and are based on the child's direct experience with phenomena rather than on his reading about or talking about science. Because the observation is individual and is based on what the child has done, a report of what he has observed can be neither right nor wrong in an absolute sense. It may be verbal or nonverbal—the latter, for example, in the case of the kindergarten children who sort objects into groups by properties. The teacher can look at their sortings and immediately realize the property used by an individual child. The child frequently is not able to tell the teacher how he sorted the objects. At this level the child is intimately involved in his experience. According to the work of Piaget and others, some of the developmental learnings contributed by such activity will not be evident verbally for a number of years.

This fourth involvement is most important and valuable to the child but is not a panacea which solves all the problems of developing a science program. The child also needs guidance in his development and must be able to relate the experiences of his involvement into an overall developing structure which is the science program.

RELATION BETWEEN THE DEGREES OF INVOLVEMENT

The delineation of these four degrees of involvement has purposely separated them and described each as if it existed independently of the other three. This helps to point out the values and shortcomings of each degree. At present, science programs in the elementary school generally include at least the first three levels of involvement and sometimes even some work on the fourth. Usually none of these exists alone since children read about science, discuss what they have read in class, and may even see a demonstration of an experiment related to what they have read. The fourth level is somewhat rarer in the present elementary science program. Ideally, the science program should include a mixture of all four degrees of involvement. Reading about science, discussion, and demonstration can be used to foster the development of situations in which children can explore the natural environment through the individualized direct laboratory approach described as level four.

The use of the educational film in elementary science has been left out of this specification of degrees of involvement of the child. The reason for this is that the film as a medium cuts across and operates on all four levels. At its worst the film is essentially a talking book presenting an illustrated lecture. These films are characterized by a narrator who dominates the situation and actually distracts one's attention from the visual presentation. In addition the film cannot respond to children in the class and so is quite remote. At the other end of the scale, the film can be used as a source of data providing experimental information for all children in the class. For example, in cases where equipment is too expensive or dangerous for use in the classroom, a film can present the experiment and the child can observe carefully and obtain the data needed either to draw conclusions or to carry out further experiments. Such films are characterized by a minimal amount of narration and the creative use of the visual medium.

Another important use of the film, especially in the life sciences, is to present the child with a record of the behavior or even complete life cycle of certain animals and/or plants. These can be animals or plants which either do not live in the environment of the children or are too large or dangerous to have around for close first-hand observation. Here the film provides information which forms the basis of a discussion about the given animal or plant and which in this case is unavailable in any other form. Also, such techniques as time-lapse photography provide the opportunity for compressing events into a shorter time thus increasing the number of organisms it is possible to study carefully. The film, then, can be a most valuable resource when used properly, but it also has the possibility of being no more than a talking book.

Instead of organizing the classroom around the textbook, it is preferable to let the direct involvement and experience of the children on level four trigger reading, discussing, demonstrating, and using of film. Then, for example, the child is reading a science book to obtain further information about something he has experienced in the classroom laboratory. No longer is his reading about a verbal abstraction referred to as science, but rather he reads to help enlarge upon his direct experience. A discussion which comes about as a result of experience can be quite different from the sterile, teacher-dominated, fishing expedition described earlier. Now groups of children who have had similar or contrasting experience can actually discuss what they have observed and can attempt to see the relationships between various individual observations. The teacher can take a vital part in such a discussion, acting not so much as a source of information but as an informed individual who asks the kinds of questions which lead either to a synthesis of the material observed by individuals or to a clearly defined need for more observation before such a synthesis can be reached. Demonstrations, whether teacher- or student-run, take on a new role when the science program is based on this fourth level of individual involvement. The demonstration is now used for one of the following purposes:

1. The verification of observations already made by individuals. This can be done either when controversy exists and the demonstration is used as a proof situation or when an individual repeats his work for the information of the group.

2. The presentation of an experiment closely related to the experience the pupils have participated in directly. This is done either because safety factors demand that the teacher carry out the experiment or the cost of the equipment involved makes it too expensive for individual pupils to use in quantity. This latter is one of the situations in which the film can be most helpful in providing the experience.

3. The experimentation or presentation of experience of such a nature that it is impractical to have everyone carry it out, for example, the observation over a month or more of what happens to a given plant or animal under certain conditions. Since checks will of necessity be periodic and other science activities will take place in the interim, it is usually not feasible to have each child set up the situation. One note of caution is necessary here. The over-enthusiastic acceptance of these conditions to determine when a demonstration is necessary can lead to a program devoid of individual experience in science. It is always less expensive, less time-consuming, and less messy to carry out a demonstration rather than to provide a situation in which individuals can experience science directly.

The need of the young learner for this direct experience is great and should be the factor which restricts the demonstration to those situations which meet the criteria just described. For example, the following reconstruction from an observer's report describes a first grade classroom in the SCIS program:

Each pupil has on his desk an assortment of objects, ten or twelve in number: bits of metal, paper, wood, plastic, and stone. He has collected these during a trip or object hunt around the school grounds. The problem is to manipulate the objects and discover different bases for grouping them. As the teacher looks over their shoulders, he finds that one pupil has divided his collection into three piles: bulky objects in one group, small ones in another, and medium-sized ones in a third. Another pupil has divided his objects into two piles, one of heavy objects, one of light objects. And one little girl has discovered that her objects can be classified according to color, light or dark, and according to surface texture, rough or smooth—and she's now separating them into piles of metal, paper, wood, plastic, glass and stone.

Choosing objects to study

The children in this classroom are deeply involved in two important aspects of basic science. On the one hand, they are analyzing, observing, noting details, testing various approaches and possibilities, and recording data. Later they will analyze their data and attempt to draw appropriate conclusions. One can refer to these activities as *processes* of science. When pursued systematically, they constitute the so-called scientific method.

On the other hand, the pupils are acquiring fundamental concepts about matter and its properties—concepts which are basic, moreover, to the *structure* of science and which run like girders through its edifice. As the pupils progress in science, they will encounter these ideas more and more frequently and in ever-more-complex applications. These children are working on the fourth level of individual involvement in science.

The adoption of this philosophy of and approach to science teaching makes impossible the separation of process goals from content goals, or either one from concept development. These three basic ingredients of the science program are completely interwoven and intermingled. No one ingredient can be isolated from the others as a means for building the science program. When the individual child is working with systems of objects in order to observe natural phenomena, he is caught up in the intricate web which is content, process, and concept development. Any attempt to separate one from the others usually leads to sterility accompanied by a significant increase in the use of words to talk about science and a decrease in the activities which allow the individual to experience natural phenomena directly.

The structuring of a science program during which the individual's opportunities to experience science at the fourth level are maximized is not an easy task. It involves not only the careful development of curriculum materials and techniques, but also requires a re-thinking on the part of the teacher of his role in the classroom. This topic will be explored more completely in the next chapter.

THE LEARNER IN THE SCIS PROGRAM

The Science Curriculum Improvement Study is developing a program which fosters the development of situations in which children can have the kinds of direct experiences which constitute the total involvement of the child in the science program. The following excerpts taken from the reports of observers in classrooms where the SCIS program is undergoing trial and evaluation clearly show the attainment of many of the goals described in this chapter. After each excerpt is a short analysis of the situation in relation to these goals.

1. Observing Mealworms: Second Grade Exploratory Work in The Life Sciences

This description of an experience in her own classroom was written by a second-grade teacher in Berkeley, California.

Each child in the class had been given a Petri dish containing about ten mealworms. After a few weeks of observation and discussion, most of the mealworms had changed into beetles. The children had enjoyed immensely the experience of observing the mealworms in their different stages of development.

The adult beetles interested them; however, they became very interested in getting more mealworms. We had a discussion in class about how we might be able to get more. The class was about equally split into three groups, each having its own theory. The first group thought that if we waited long enough the beetles would change back into mealworms, in a fashion similar to but in reverse of what they had observed as a mealworm changed into a beetle. The second group decided that the beetles would lay eggs, which would hatch, and out would come new mealworms. The last group felt that the beetles would just lay live mealworms. Each group felt very strong that its idea would prove correct, so each group decided to set up an experiment for proof.

The children decided each group should have exactly twenty beetles in its containers. I asked them why they chose that particular number of beetles. One child replied, "Everyone should have the same amount so we all have the same chance." Another child said, "If we have twenty, we'll have enough because you have to have quite a bit so we can be sure they are mixed up." I asked him why it was important that you mix them up. He answered, "If you don't mix them up, you might have just one kind. You can wait all year and nothing will happen." He related this to his experience with guinea pigs when he had waited all year and nothing had happened.

Each group observed the containers for three or four more weeks, and nothing observable seemed to be occurring. I asked them what they thought about their experiment. One child said, "You have to be patient. It probably doesn't happen so fast." Most of the children agreed, so they decided to give the beetles more time.

We discussed the experiment again at a later time. By then most of the children felt something should be happening, although it appeared not to be. One child said, "Maybe we didn't think of the right way. There might be some special way and we didn't think of it." Another child said, "Maybe they have to have special things like dirt or leaves or something like that." The children discussed ways we might be able to find out. Some suggested asking a person who knew all about mealworms. Others suggested looking in a book about mealworms.

Although we never got any new mealworms from the beetles we had, the children did not give up and had continued interest throughout their experiment. After trying out their own ideas, they were ready to seek help from other sources.

The children had worked with SCIS materials in the physical sciences during that year and the previous year. From the foregoing material, it is clear that these children were used to having a direct involvement in their science program. In the terms of Piaget, they not only wanted to have "experience"—the observation of the mealworms—but they were also "active" in the sense that they discussed the problem, divided into groups with divergent opinions, and set up experiments to prove their points of view. This setting-up of experiments to settle a controversy is a most important indication of the effect the program had on the learner. Since the greater part of the children's science program included direct involvement in working with systems and objects of interest, they naturally turned to this approach in order to prove their conceptions of how to obtain more mealworms from beetles. The portioning out by agreement of twenty beetles to each group is an indication of their understanding of the need to have similar situations in order to compare the results of the different groups.

After a period of time, when nothing happened, the children gave further evidence of their sophistication by suggesting that maybe there were some other variables (dirt, leaves, etc.) which needed to be controlled. Their lack of success in the experiments they set up was undoubtedly frustrating, but the teacher wisely channeled this frustration by encouraging suggestions for a further study of mealworms through books and even by calling in a consultant. The children would probably now read a book, listen to a talk, or watch a movie about mealworms or even the life cycles of other animals with interest and enthusiasm.

The reason for this enthusiasm would be, of course, that the children's direct involvement in the study of the life cycle of one animal developed a foundation based on experience for their interest in further information about the life cycle of that animal or other animals. One must keep in mind, however, that reading, talking, or watching a movie about mealworms or other animals should continue only so long as the children's involvement based on experience remains. Fairly soon further direct experience should be provided as the basis for continued development of the child's participation in the science program.

2. OBSERVING EVIDENCE OF INTERACTION: THIRD GRADE *Interaction and Systems* PROGRAM

FIGURE 7

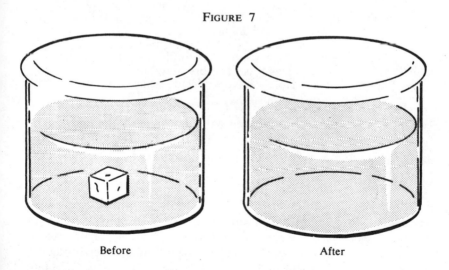

Before   After

The picture story in Figure 7 provoked the following dialogue between the children and the teacher. The class agreed that something happened in the story and then went on to describe the objects in the story. The object in the jar in the first picture caused some disagreement. The responses quoted here were given by different children.

Pupil: It's sugar. It's a sugar cube. A sugar cube breaks up in water.
Pupil: It's ice, and the ice melts in water.
Pupil: No, if it was ice you would have more water.
Pupil: It looks like sugar. It's a sugar cube because it's square.
Teacher: Could ice be square?
Pupil: Yes, but not all the time, so it's probably sugar.
Pupil: It's a dice.
Pupil: No, dice doesn't melt.
Pupil: Somebody might have taken it out of the water.
Pupil: It's not ice. Ice would float at the top.
Teacher: Will sugar float at the top?

The children say no, sugar will not float at the top, but they do not seem to accept this idea.

Pupil: It's soap, because of the bubbles coming off.
Pupil: I measured. The height of water in both is the same, about sixteen inches.
Pupil: If you drop in sugar, it won't float up.
Pupil: It's not soap. Soap takes too long a time to dissolve and forms lots of bubbles and lather.
Pupil to teacher: Do we have to decide what it is?

The teacher suggested they write down what they thought was in the jar. She placed on the board the names of all the possibilities they had mentioned except the dice which had been rejected by the class. There was no emphasis on the problem of the jar versus the water in the jar.

The next day the teacher did an experiment in which she set up three jars of water and had children carry out each of the possible experiments. One of the children who thought the object in the jar was ice obtained a piece from the school cafeteria for the experiment. One child brought a piece of sugar, and another brought a piece of soap. As the child placed the sugar cube, ice, or soap into the water, he carried the jar around the room so that the whole class could see. After observing the experiments, the class decided that it was sugar in the jar pictured in their manual. From the discussion, it appeared that what convinced most of the children was that the sugar cube gave off bubbles in the water and the picture showed bubbles coming from the object. The fact that sugar sinks in water while ice floats was not of great importance to this group in coming to its decision.

The teacher could have told them what was in the jar at the very beginning and saved class time. Instead, thirty third-graders spent half an hour observing, analyzing their observations, and defending or modifying the conclusions they reached on the basis of their observations. Here one sees the discussion and demonstration used effectively to increase interest and involvement on the part of the class. The teacher's acceptance of all possibilities the first day set the stage for the demonstration on the next day. The children gained a great deal through being socially interactive with one another. Even though the rather obvious adult reason (ice floats, sugar sinks) was not important to the children, their reasoning was accurate and was based on direct observation. For these children, observation is an important means for providing evidence about natural phenomena.

The following shorter excerpts of conversations or descriptions of conversations between children or between children and teacher indicate the kind of social interaction and communication which is so important to the intellectual development of the young child. Each of these is based on some experience or experiences the children had. This direct involvement seems to be the most effective means for developing situations in which children will collaborate and interact with each other and the teacher. The other important characteristic which comes through is the flexibility in thinking which has been fostered in these children because of their direct involvement.

OBSERVING A POTTED PLANT: A FIRST GRADE CLASS

Teacher: Does this plant have roots?
Pupil: Yes, in the dirt. They're down at the bottom.
Teacher: How can we find out?
Pupil: Water it every day. If the plants have water, they have roots.
Teacher: Yes, I read that too, but how can we find out?
Pupil: You could get a shovel and you could put on your garden gloves and just dig around the dirt.

Following this suggestion, the plant was removed from its pot, and the children became very excited when they saw the roots.

Pupil: The plant is big where the roots start.
Teacher: If I had never seen a root, how would you describe it
             to me?
Pupil: They feel rough.
Pupil: They look white with brown from the dirt on them.
Pupil: They hang straight down like a banana.
Pupil: They feel like veins.

Discussion and questions are fostered by the direct involvement with
the shells

4. SORTING OBJECTS INTO GROUPS

A first grader, after returning from an object hunt, proceeded to
sort the objects she had collected into two groups. The first group
contained some sticks and a piece of string; the second, leaves and
blades of grass. When asked how she had sorted her collection, she
explained that she had put the straight objects into one group and
the green objects into another. Her teacher picked up a leaf that had
a rather long stem and asked which group it belonged in. After

regarding the object thoughtfully, the little girl broke off the stem, put it into the straight group, and put the leaf into the green group. When asked about the blades of grass, she replied, "They're straight and green and so they belong in the middle."

5. OBSERVING GROWTH OF SEEDS

A group of second graders was discussing a collection of seeds planted on the previous day. When asked whether they had noticed any evidence of interaction, one child replied, "Yes, one of my seeds popped up out of the ground. It's not growing, but maybe the water floated the seed up to the top. The seed popping up is evidence of interaction between the water and the seed." Another child suggested that if there were another seed growing under the one that popped up, it could have pushed the top one out. He called the seed coming out of the ground evidence of interaction and as objects in the system, chose the two seeds, water, and the stem that did the pushing.

SUMMARY

In this chapter, the learner's relationship to the science program has been looked at. After discussing several levels of involvement, the importance of pupils having direct experience with the objects and systems in the environment has been developed. The value of social interaction—that is, the discussions among children and the collaboration of a group of children in an experiment—has been developed. Specific examples from classrooms participating in the experimental work of the Science Curriculum Improvement Study have been cited in order to indicate the effect of this kind of an approach on a group of learners. Looking to the future, further study is needed of the ways in which young children learn so that the kind of direct experience described in this chapter can be provided in an atmosphere which maximizes the opportunities for learning on a level which can be meaningful for the child.

V

The Role of The Teacher

THE TEACHER

The first three chapters developed the historical and conceptual basis for the Science Curriculum Improvement Study. The role of the learner in relation to such a program was analyzed in Chapter IV. In this chapter the role of the teacher in bringing the program and the learner together will be described.

As the adult directly responsible for the presentation of the educational program to the student, the teacher in any classroom occupies a most important role. In elementary science, and especially in a curriculum like SCIS which not only has long-range content goals but also a long-term objective of changing adult behavior (developing functional scientific literacy), the actions and attitudes of the teacher become essential to the success of the program.

Some investigators have proposed or even developed allegedly "teacher proof" or totally student-centered programs of instruction. Much of the material labeled "programed instruction" gives one this impression. In certain specific areas it has proved rather successful, especially in the teaching of a given skill such as the use of the slide rule. In general its lack of spontaneity and adaptability for different groups of learners has tended to prevent the widespread adoption of programed instruction as a general teaching technique. Other attempts to build totally child-centered programs in which a teacher is unnecessary have proved unsuccessful because they negate an important aspect in the intellectual development of a child: In order for learning to take place, the child must be involved in the experience, as described in Chapter IV. The acceptance of this point of view leads to a very important role for the teacher—that of observer of the children's present experience who analyzes these observations in order to develop the insight and understanding necessary for making the choice of relevant future experiences for them.

This is a continuing process and the planning for tomorrow's or next week's experience must be based on the outcomes of today's experience. Even if one could control the *outcome* of the experience —impossible if the children are given freedom and encouragement to investigate a given situation on their own—how can one expect to control or presuppose the *reactions* of the pupils to the experience? If the producer of a child-centered or "teacher proof" curriculum has any objectives at all, he must expect to specify both the outcome of each experience and the pupils' reactions to it. The task of teacher training to make available the kind of teacher described in this chapter is demanding. It is, however, attainable, whereas the "teacher proof" or totally child-centered curriculum which does not need the teacher is unattainable because one cannot specify both the outcomes of and the individual pupil's reactions to experiences.

This concept of the teacher's role is important when one considers any group of learners, but becomes particularly critical when one thinks about the learning patterns of elementary school children. Especially in the early years of the elementary school, the child is functionally illiterate in regard to the printed word. That is, although he is learning to read, the child has significant problems in following written instructions. He has a lack of understanding about how different statements fit together. Furthermore, his vocabulary and ability to express himself in writing are severely limited. Oral and even gestural language are a much more secure and powerful means of communication for the young child. The presence in the classroom of an adult leader (the teacher) capable of listening to, analyzing, and guiding this communication, which can by design be based on actual experience, leads to the further development of understanding on the part of the children. Child-to-child communication is also a most important aspect of the operation of a science classroom. The experience forming the basis for this communication should be structured by an effective teacher. She should understand both the content and process aspects of the subject of science for which she is building the classroom instructional program. The responsibility for the actual planning of the science lesson in the classroom rests with the teacher.

PLANNING THE SCIENCE LESSON

Some general considerations regarding the planning of the science lessons in the classroom should be kept in mind. The Science Curriculum Improvement Study or any other science program should provide for many kinds of activities: teacher demonstrations, pupil experiments, recording observations, interpreting illustrations, pupil discussions, and so on. These activities form the basis for classroom planning.

As the lessons are planned, keep in mind the needs of the pupils and the overall structure of the science material chosen for study. One may like to think of the science lessons as having three main parts: the introduction, in which use is made of a current incident involving the pupils to set the stage for the activity; the main body of the lesson, in which the content is organized for invention or discovery; and the conclusion, in which pupils are oriented toward the next science lesson and toward applying their new ideas outside science class.

The introduction and conclusion will be determined as the lesson is planned. The introduction may be based on the review of experiments in a previous science class or on an event in the class that is not directly related to science. The conclusion may involve a restatement of certain questions that were asked, it may consist of a challenge to tentative conclusions reached by the class, or it may relate the class experience to some facets of the pupils' daily lives.

There seems to be a tradition in education today that there be no "loose ends" at the conclusion of a lesson: There should be a single answer for each question, there should be a verbal summary of the lesson's objectives. This tendency has even been given a name—lysiphobia, the fear of leaving loose ends. A good lesson has a conclusion, but that conclusion should orient the children toward future work. Loose ends—ambiguities, uncertainties, disagreements—can be emphasized because the interest they create is a strong stimulus to further investigation. The children's ability to resolve uncertainties by themselves will, in the end, give them greater satisfaction. Encourage them to do so.

It will be apparent that some of the children's experiments do not have clean-cut results. In that case, interested groups should be invited to explore some of the possible interpretations or explanations that they or other children may suggest. To give them a chance for further experimentation and observation, leave the materials in a readily accessible place such as a science corner or science table. Since it is impossible to foresee which details of the experiments will give rise to further work, enthusiasm, leadership, and opportunism on the teacher's part will be important in making this aspect of the science program a success.

The main body of the lesson should be treated in a way that depends on the aims of the activities. At some times work of a *discovery* nature forms the basis for the lesson. This is designed to broaden the children's background of experience and to let them apply their new ideas. Let them look again and again if their

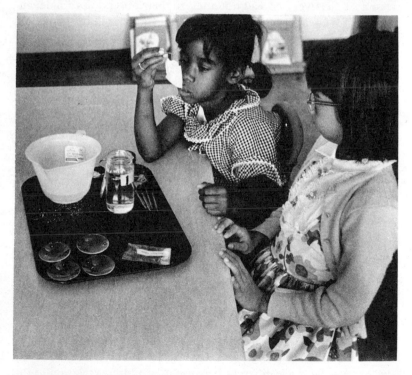

Experimentation with substances to discover ideas of solutions and evaporation

initial curiosity is not satisfied after one opportunity to observe. One should feel free to question and to suggest new paths of thinking. Be responsive to their questions and encourage curiosity. An answer to all questions should not be expected, however, and new questions rather than conclusions should be drawn from the experiments.

In this work, the children should be encouraged to report their observations frankly. They should describe what they see, feel, hear, smell, and so on. The children should not get the feeling that a certain answer is expected; if they do, they will give that answer and stop making observations. For this reason, one should ask, "What have you observed today?" Then each child can give an honest answer. Some teachers ask, "What have we learned today?" This question makes people try to remember what they were *supposed* to have learned. They will repeat the teacher's statement of the lesson's objectives and will not analyze their observations independently. If the teacher feels a certain statement should be made, it is often best for her to make it outright and not to shop among the pupils for it.

At other times one will provide a term for a new concept and a concrete definition for the meaning of the term. Such a new concept may be called a conceptual invention because it was once invented by a scientist; now, of course, it is "new" only for the pupils. Lessons in which a new term is defined are *invention* lessons. Most children form stable and usable concepts only when they have a verbal label to help them focus their attention on the concept. One should not hesitate to be clear and explicit when giving definitions, and the definition should be repeated several times if necessary. Remember, children can and should make their own observations, but they cannot, in general, invent new language by themselves.

When one introduces an invention, it should be phrased as a suggestion. The children should be invited to think about their observations in terms of that invention. As an example is met during subsequent lessons, the children will find the invention a useful tool for the description and analysis of phenomena; through this activity they will discover and assimilate the meaning of the invention.

The classroom settings required by invention lessons and by discovery lessons are different because the children's relation to the teacher is different. In an invention lesson, it is helpful to cluster the children close to the teacher so they can follow the demonstrations and focus their attention more strongly; their desks are unnecessary and get in the way. In a discovery lesson, by contrast, it is helpful to distribute the children around the classroom so they can work independently or in small groups and concentrate on their own experiments. These and other classroom arrangements should be used to adapt the atmosphere of the room to the needs of the planned lessons.

The ability to improvise and to depart from the lesson plans will enable one to better meet the needs of the pupils. Sometimes the children's expressions and verbal responses will indicate that they are not ready for the introduction of a new concept. In that situation, it is better to drop the invention and return to the introductory activities. At other times, the pupils will ask questions that do not lead in the direction indicated by the planned procedures. If that happens, one should permit oneself the pleasure of trying these side trips. They may give rise to fruitful experiences. Pupils can be encouraged to explore still other questions on their own.

When a child answers a question incorrectly, one should respond in such a way that he does not become discouraged from contributing to discussions in the future. It is important to try to recognize the reason for the error—it may be lack of attention to the question, careless or faulty observation, or still another reason. In case of a misunderstanding, one may have to provide a quick explanation. A careless observation can often be improved with repetition. Sometimes it is best to let the "wrong" answer stand for the time being and return to the problem area later. Sometimes mistakes can be used to stimulate debate and mutual criticism among the children.

More important than any of these remarks is that the teacher thinks of the science course as *his* course. One should enjoy the teaching. The experiments the children perform, the questions they ask, the understandings they develop will help make the science lessons fun for the pupils and, therefore, more challenging and enjoyable for the leader.

The role implied for the teacher in this discussion is quite different from the one-to-one correspondence between teaching and talking which is all too often the observable situation in public schools today. One infrequently observes a teacher who is a good listener in her own classroom. At present, this skill is not stressed in teacher education programs. It is true that elementary school teachers usually do ask questions and engage themselves in discussions with pupils. They do not lecture like college professors who rarely give their students a chance to speak at all. Unfortunately, the questions are usually asked to get at an answer that is already formulated in the teacher's mind or to make a point of the teacher's own choosing. Most teachers rarely ask questions because they are curious to know what the pupils think, believe, or have observed. And pupils adapt quickly to this situation; after a few years in school answering questions is for them more a mind-reading proposition than a matter of reasoning about the substance of a problem.

QUESTION-ASKING

Question-asking can and should be a major aspect of the teacher's planning for the progress of the science program in the classroom. Many objectives can be furthered by the wise use of questions. Many questions can be grouped as divergent in that they lead to further questions, cause children to carry out or plan experiences with equipment and materials, or foster the kind of inquiry that causes children to research information in the library. All of these questions foster thinking, will probably enlarge the scope of the material being studied, and usually deepen the interest of at least some children in the topic under study. Other questions can be classified as convergent, that is, they tend to cause children to summarize and draw conclusions. After sufficient experience on the children's part, such questions can prove most helpful in bringing about the combination and recombination of experiences which lead to generalization and understanding. Questions which aim at the simple recall of facts probably fall in this convergent category. Their importance can be limited, and they should be used with caution. Question-asking or posing of problems is an integral part of all evaluation procedures. The next chapter, which is devoted to evaluation, will consider this point in depth.

Examples from The Classroom

The following examples from classrooms using the Science Curriculum Improvement Study program illustrate the kind of question-asking one would like to observe in all elementary school classrooms. The example is cited and followed by a short explanatory and/or interpretive statement. Questions are marked with a "D" or a "C" to indicate their divergency or convergency.

Variation in Number of Beans in Bean Pods: In a second grade classroom, the teacher introduced an activity on the variation of the number of beans in a collection of bean pods (those found in a can) by opening the can, removing the beans, and giving each child three beans. The following discussion takes place.

Teacher: How are the beans alike?[D]
Pupil: All sort of fat.
Pupil: Skinny.
Pupil: They have seeds in them.
Teacher: How do you know?[D]
Pupil: I can see in the little hole.
Pupil: They have lines [continuing with "how are they alike"].
Pupil: None have holes.
Pupil: Have juice.
Pupil: Mine are squiggly.
Pupil: Smell good.
Pupil: All have points on end.
Teacher: How are they different?[D]
Pupil: One has a circle here and others have points on the ends.
Teacher: What do you mean, "here?"[C]
Pupil: On the end.
Pupil: One is light green, one is dark green, and one is very dark green.
Teacher: There is a difference in color, then.
Pupil: This one is bumpy and this is not.
Pupil: One has a seed at the end.
Pupil: Mine has a little part that is broken off.
Pupil: One is squishy.
Pupil: Some are dry and some are wet.
Pupil: Some are rough and some are smooth.
Pupil: They have different lengths.
Teacher: How much different? How many found their beans to be different lengths?[C] [About 1/3 did]. Is there as much difference in length as with pea pods we used before?[C]

The objective of having the children describe the properties of the bean pods was accomplished effectively by using the comparative but divergent questions, "How are the beans alike?" and "How are they different?" Notice how much richer the responses to such questions were as compared to a question like "What color are the beans?" which can only bring about the response "green." The teacher also uses questions to clarify responses or to check on the accuracy of observation. Again, "How do you know?" in response to "They have seeds in them" brings about the response, "I can see in the little hole" which is possible with some canned green beans. The meaning of the term *here* is determined by a simple question by the teacher. Both of these clarifying questions focus attention on a specific aspect of the work and simply provide more information within the context of property determination. In one sense they are convergent (clarifying the child's statement), but they do not cut off discussion at that point. The last question is intended to introduce the next task, which is to have every child identify each one of his bean pods by some comparative characteristic such as length, color, etc. This information will then be recorded in the student manual.

Goldfish and Air: The following sequence took place in a third-grade class. The children were observing and setting up experiments with goldfish during a number of sessions to test the possibility of using these organisms in the life sciences program of SCIS. They had raised questions and set up experiments about the question of whether or not fish need air. The children seemed sure that fish need air, so the teacher decided to explore the question of *how* they obtain it.

Teacher: How do goldfish get air?[D]
Pupil: The fish takes water in his mouth and by moving his stomach back and forth pushes it past his gills. The gills take the air out of the water. The fish then takes more water in through his mouth.
Teacher: That's very interesting. What do some other people think?[D]
Pupil: When the fish needs air, he comes to the top and sticks his mouth out and gulps some.
Pupil: I saw my goldfish at home do that. [Through discussion, it became apparent that more than half the class agreed with this second observation about gulping.]
Teacher: How many fish are there in the ocean?[C]
Pupil: Thousands.
Pupil: Millions!

Teacher: It must be quite a sight when they all come up to the top, stick out their mouths, and gulp some air.
Pupil: Oh, they do it far out where you can't see them.
Pupil: They come up at night to gulp air.

An important role is played by the teacher in this sequence. In response to the original question, a child gives a sophisticated answer about the use of gills. Instead of accepting this and going on, the teacher is noncommittal and asks for other ideas. It soon becomes apparent that more than half of the children think the fish gulp air. The teacher then asks the question about the number of fish in the ocean in order to build up to the discrepancy of all the fish in the ocean surfacing to gulp air. Although two children try to give explanations, an obvious problem with the gulping-air hypothesis becomes very clear after this interchange between teacher and pupil. (Most of the class laughed at the idea of all those fish surfacing.) The problem is not solved since nothing has been done to support the original and accurate observation. By not accepting this answer right away and by taking time to unearth what many of the other children thought, the teacher is able to raise serious doubts about an incorrect but popular point of view. The stage has been set so that further experience observing the fish can be used to help develop a clearer understanding of the way in which they breathe. For example, fish can be placed in a capped jar completely filled with water. Children are then asked to look for new evidence.

Ice Calorimetry: The following report from a fourth-grade class shows the use of the question as the means for organizing the lesson. The children are working with ice and other objects, and the teacher is leading up to introducing the amount of ice melted as an operational definition of energy.

Teacher: What do you think causes ice to melt?[D]
Pupil: Air.
Pupil: Air.
Pupil: Heat.
Pupil: Heat and air.
Pupil: Air.
Pupil: Air.
Pupil: Some things that interact with ice.
Pupil: Weight.
Pupil: Air, heat, and things that interact with ice.
Pupil: Anything that's not as cold as ice.

Teacher: How many agree that anything that is not as cold as ice will melt ice?[C] [All agree.]
Teacher: What else do you think causes ice to melt?
Pupil: Heat.
Pupil: Temperature.
Teacher: What do you mean by that?[D]
Pupil: Sometimes an object is hot and sometimes it's cold.
Teacher: In our experiments, we have found whenever we put an object with ice, if the object is warmer than ice, what happens to the temperature of the object?[C]
Pupil: Gets cooler.
Teacher: Do you suppose a bigger object will melt more ice than a smaller object? [D] [Three-quarters of the class say a bigger object will melt more ice.]
Pupil: It depends on the weight. [The teacher shows two aluminum objects to the class, one large, one small.]
Teacher: Which one will melt more ice?[C]
Pupil: Big one.
Pupil: I disagree; sometimes the bigger one might be colder.
Pupil: It depends on how much colder.
Teacher: What should you ask me about these objects?[C]
Pupil: What the temperature is.
Teacher: If they are at the same temperature, which would melt more ice?[C]
Pupil: The big one. [All agree.]

Throughout this sequence, the teacher's use of the question to obtain further information about the children's thinking in order to form further questions is apparent. These lead to a review of prior experience and, finally, to a higher level of understanding about the original problem. When children try to use words like "temperature," they are challenged to determine if actual understanding exists. The teacher can help to develop the definition of the term, based on the children's experience.

The importance of question-asking and the purposes for which one asks questions cannot be overemphasized in regard to the consideration of the role of teacher of elementary science.

Precautions in Question-Asking

There are, however, a number of precautionary measures one should take in the use of questions as a major aspect of one's approach to elementary science teaching:

1. Questions that are extremely broad and not related directly to

the experience of young children tend to be very confusing and overwhelming to them. For example, the question "How do fish get air?" mentioned on p. 88 must be preceded by many opportunities for the children to observe fish if their answers are to have any meaning. In some cases—such as the melting of an ice cube—questions can be used to explore the children's existing preconceptions based on experiences in or out of school. When doing this, one must be very careful not to ask the broad, overwhelming questions.

It takes energy to melt ice

2. The technique of tabling a correct answer (as in the case of the fish) in order to explore the other children's conception of the problem is valuable, but must be used carefully. Young children, and even many adults, have a tendency to accept as fact what their peers agree to en masse. If the teacher waits too long before showing (preferably by experience or discussion) the fallacy in a popular point of view, the children may latch onto it as fact. Particularly dangerous is an attitude of accepting all answers without

attempting to differentiate between meaningful and nonmeaningful responses. This leads to misconceptions and misunderstanding and negates the teacher's leadership role in the classroom.

3. Frequently one will use a question in order to encourage a child to explain his point of view more carefully or even to cause a child to reconsider what seems to be an inaccurate or irrelevant point of view. This is a reasonable and meaningful use of the question-asking technique. Pupils should not, however, get the idea that every time the teacher asks questions it means she is displeased or not satisfied with a previous comment. One nice way to prevent this from happening is to ask the same kinds of questions of good students who have given perfectly acceptable answers. This technique has the added advantage of encouraging children to have confidence in their ideas. By attempting to support the position they have taken, they will rethink their own ideas and so develop a deeper understanding of the subject under discussion.

4. A child's direct observations should not be evaluated as right or wrong. Instead, a question, such as "What is your evidence?" can be used to focus the child's attention on what has actually happened. This is particularly helpful when it appears there is a clear discrepancy between the event and the child's observation and report of it. Children who have made conflicting observations of the same or similar events can be asked for the evidence on which they base their reports. This will help to define the areas of disagreement and may lead to either a resolution of the controversy or to the proposal of additional experiences in order to help settle the disagreement.

THE TEACHER'S ROLE AND ATTITUDE

This question-asking and the related and important function of listening to children must take place in an atmosphere that encourages observation of and actual experience with natural phenomena by children. The elementary school classroom must essentially be a laboratory in which children have experiences with the objects and systems of science under the direction of an informed teacher who is a careful listener and guide.

This is not to suggest, however, that the teacher's role is a passive one. On the contrary, she is the individual responsible for maintaining the conceptual continuity of the program. Only through such leadership can the objectives of the program be realized. The classroom is the laboratory where children can make discoveries and gain experience with natural phenomena. The teacher is the leader whose job is not primarily to *tell* children about science or to *listen* to them while they *read* about science, but rather to *observe* children while they are individually *involved* with science. Pupils are encouraged to experiment to find answers to their questions. The teacher uses her questions as a means for opening up new possibilities, enlarging upon discussed ideas, and in general encouraging children to probe further and think again about the observations they have made or will make of natural phenomena.

Another aspect of the teacher's role in science is related to but somewhat different from the area of question-asking techniques. This involves the teacher's attitudes and actions while individual pupils or small groups of children are at work observing and acting upon organisms and systems during the laboratory part of the science program. As developed in Chapter IV, this is the most important part of the science program; the child is actually involved with natural phenomena, and the role of the adult leader, therefore, becomes very important.

One extreme of this role is passivity. The teacher responds to most questions or comments from the children with "that's nice" or "keep working." By trying not to interfere with the children's work, this teacher assumes she should melt into the background and take no role in the situation whatsoever. She is present to maintain order, protect the safety of the children, and dispense materials or supplies when necessary. At the other end of the scale is the teacher who assumes that because the children have little or no experience working in science, the equipment is expensive, and/or time is short, she ought to direct the children. The teacher gives explicit instructions for every move and tends to sound like a talking recipe book. Usually this instruction includes not only what to do, but also a "clear" description of what is to be observed and an indication or statement of the conclusions to be drawn from the observation.

Neither of these extremes is acceptable in today's elementary science classroom, but one cannot entirely reject them both. The ideal teacher should melt into the background when, for example, children are making and recording their own observations. Conversely, if the experience includes the use of new or complex materials, she should explicitly instruct the children in how to use them but not in what outcome to expect. The teacher must be responsible for the safety and well-being of the children in the class, but she must insure that the possibility of a meaningful experience is not removed from the situation.

What, then, is the role of the teacher when the children are actively involved in working with equipment and materials in the science classroom? As indicated, it includes some aspects of both extremes described. It is different, however, in that every action by the teacher in the classroom laboratory should be guided by a single objective: To increase the child's opportunity to observe the system under study in a manner that makes the system meaningful to him. Before any inferences can be made or conclusions drawn, it is essential that this objective be reached. In the ideal situation, then, the teacher responds to questions with another question or with a comment, and, again ideally, causes the children to see the situation in another light and perhaps even to repeat an experiment in a different way. For example, a child who reports an observation completely out of line with those of the other students is not scolded for carelessness or lectured on the need to work more carefully. Rather, the discrepancy between his observation and those of many others is pointed out, and he is asked to reproduce his experiment or give other evidence of the reproducibility of his observation. In trying the experiment again, the child will probably discover his error (if there was one) and come up with a result more in line with the group's data. He may, on the other hand, provide new information which is helpful in understanding the phenomenon under study. Instead of being punitive, this experience has become a learning situation for the whole group, since one of the foundations of scientific activity is the need for reproducible observations. And even more important, the child's confidence in his own work is not undermined by authority but is modified by his own further experience. In such a situation, the teacher has served a most important and far from passive function.

When a child is hopelessly confused or simply cannot begin operating with the material at hand, the teacher must again step in and exert leadership. Rather than tell the child what to do, which would probably do little to help him handle the next situation, the teacher must consider the source of his difficulties. Through questions and an individual discussion with the child, she should be able to determine the source of his confusion. If the task is too much for the child, then other experiences which will help to develop the necessary skills and understanding needed to attack the task at hand should be suggested. If, on the other hand, it seems that the problem is a lack of understanding about a specific fact, a part of the experiment, or a given piece of apparatus, then the teacher should ask questions and work with the child using the problem-causing apparatus or whatever is needed to guide him over the hurdle. The teacher must use caution to go only as far as seems necessary and to refrain from telling the child so much that he is prevented from having the necessary experience involved in the activity.

This is not to indicate that the teacher has no responsibility for giving a complete explanation. Especially during "invention" lessons the teacher should explain in a forthright manner the necessary apparatus she is developing during the lesson. Rather than try to ask leading questions of children, it is better to state explicitly the information or explanation. Wherever possible, the explanation should be related to prior experience the children have had and should be made more meaningful by a demonstration or possibly a film. This verbal explanation on the teacher's part is helpful, not only in describing the ideas to be invented but also as an introduction to the kinds of experiences the children will have in the discovery activities which follow the invention session.

These are some of the ways in which the teacher should operate in the classroom while the children are working with materials in science. There is no precise prescription which describes what the teacher should do in every case, but clearly she must keep in mind the objective of increasing the child's opportunity for making meaningful observations of the systems under study. As long as this objective is considered and the knowledge of the individual children involved is brought to bear on each situation, the opportunities for learning will increase sharply in the science classroom. The results of these experiences, the observations made, must be incorporated into, and used to bring about the children's development of under-standing the aspects of science chosen for their study. This occurs as these observations and experiences are integrated into and form the basis for the other facets of the science program. In working with these experiences, the teacher's attitude toward and ability to use questions is, of course, most important.

SUMMARY OF TEACHER'S ROLE

In summary, the teacher's role in the SCIS science classroom can be characterized in the following terms: The classroom is considered a laboratory where children can make discoveries and gain experience about natural phenomena. The teacher is a leader whose job is not primarily to tell children about science or to listen to them while they read about science; rather, she observes and offers leadership to children while they are individually involved with science. Pupils are encouraged to experiment to find answers to their questions. The work of the children, their observations, and their questions are used as the basis for planning further science activities. Conceptual "inventions" are provided by the teacher when necessary, but are always followed by extensive opportunities for "discovery" experiences. In all of this planning and rethinking, the teacher is guided by her understanding of the overall content and structure of the subject, science, and her own developing knowledge of how young people learn it.

The actions of the teacher are what determine the "curriculum" in the classroom. By definition, for our purposes, the curriculum is an interactive concept consisting of, first, the developed knowledge of the "subject" and its relationship to children of a given age level, and, second, the knowledge of the "pupil" which helps clarify the learning capabilities of the children for whom a given science program is intended.

The subject is composed of a content factor and process factor which are totally linked to and interactive with each other. That is, there can be no dichotomy between process and content, and any attempt to separate the two leads to sterility of point of view and a proliferation of the words needed to describe the program. Once this point of view is adopted, the delineation of the subject should evolve from the basic structure of the discipline or disciplines which are components of the subject. Decisions as to what comprises the basic structure of a discipline must be left in the hands of practitioners in that discipline. In science, for example, this is the responsibility of the physicists, chemists, biologists, or other scientists. Once this structure is determined, the question of how to translate it into meaningful experiences for children of a given age group becomes real. This is the point at which the science education specialist working together with the aforementioned individuals must further define the subject and the way of approaching it with the group of children for whom the curriculum is intended, i.e., the inclusive classification of elementary, junior high, or high school level pupils, rather than the specific students of a single teacher.

The subject, therefore, is a complex whole made up of content and process factors which enable children of a chosen age level to have experience with and develop understanding of the basic structure of the discipline or disciplines which make up that subject. The complete specification of the subject utilizes the talents of the practitioner in the discipline and the curriculum specialist in the field who, working together, determine the makeup of the subject and strategy for presenting it to the intended group of learners.

The pupil aspect of the pattern is composed of a number of factors, each of which is related to the intellectual maturity of the intended learner. Intellectual maturity is defined in its broadest sense to mean, on the one hand, the specification of the kinds and levels of subject which the individual can master and, on the other, it includes a careful analysis of the impact of what is taught at any given time on the ongoing, long-term intellectual development of the individual. The understanding of the pupil aspect in the pattern depends on utilization of the research in the psychology of learning and the efforts to develop a learning theory or theories. The work of Piaget, Bruner, and others, with its emphasis on young children and how they learn, seems most promising for those interested in the pupil factor at the elementary school level.

The teacher, then, emerges as the crucial individual whose task is the day-to-day synthesis in the classroom of the two major aspects—the subject and the pupil—which comprise the science curriculum. The teacher draws upon the work of the specialists in determining the subject and upon the research contributing to an understanding of the pupil, but she alone is the individual who interacts directly with the children. For this reason the prime specialty of all elementary school teachers, science or otherwise, must be the child and how he learns. This is not to be confused with the absurdity of some self-contained classroom diehards who "teach children, not subjects." Rather, because one is interested in attaining specific short- and long-range goals in relation to an understanding of the subject, it is necessary for one to know as much as possible about the learner and his intellectual capabilities, maturation, and experience.

VI

An Initial Approach
to Evaluation

THE ROLES OF EVALUATION

In the preceding chapter, it was pointed out that the teacher's observation of the children's classroom activities constitutes a continuous evaluation of their progress. The teacher responds, both consciously and subconsciously, to her observations and adjusts the teaching program in accordance with her observations and her understanding of the aims of the teaching program.

A second kind of evaluation is a comparative study of children who have passed through different educational programs. The study has to be based on a test or measure which can discriminate desired behavior, such as effective problem-solving, analytical abilities, or creativity, from undesired behavior, such as the lack of the foregoing. Such a test presupposes a value judgment as to what constitutes desirable behavior and a psychological determination of what performance constitutes evidence that the desirable behavior will be applied in situations that call for it. An evaluation of this kind is of help to teachers and school administrators when they have to make decisions about adopting new curricula.

A third kind of evaluation, finally, is a study to determine what children have learned from a teaching unit. The answer to this question is vital for curriculum-makers, who try to influence the development of the children. They must find correlations between learning experiences and children's behavioral changes so that they may create a teaching program that achieves the desired goals.

The work done by the Science Curriculum Improvement Study in exploring and using this third kind of evaluation will be described in this chapter.

It is, unfortunately, utopian to believe that the selection of teaching goals or objectives specifies the teaching program in any clear-cut way. Only in the case of very simple skill objectives is mere practice in the desired behavior an effective teaching technique. Since our objectives are complex (they include a combination of understanding concepts, initiative in recognizing and attacking problems, and mastery of experimental techniques), the construction of a unit by the procedures described earlier is actually an experimental research project. Its outcomes can be estimated by theoretical considerations, but they cannot be foreseen precisely; they must be determined experimentally. The role of evaluation for the curriculum-maker, therefore, is to determine what children have learned. He has to find how children have changed not only with respect to the specific objectives of their most recent learning experiences, but also with respect to the more complex dimensions stated previously. This need implies that the evaluation include divergent problem situations in which children can express their originality as well as convergent problems that test more specific achievement.

There are other problems as well. First, the attainment of the general objectives just described is not directly observable. One must, therefore, decide what observable behaviors on the children's part will be accepted as evidence that the objectives have been reached. Second, the children may be affected by the teaching program in ways that are not clearly related to its objectives. It is necessary, therefore, to explore more broadly just what the children have learned. Third, it is not sufficient to determine the results of the teaching program. One must also gather information that will indicate how the teaching program should be modified so as to be more effective. This may include improving the procedures or changing the emphasis toward a somewhat different combination of objectives.

The evaluation procedures used to meet these needs are based on confronting the student with a set of experimental problems for whose solution he has to apply the concepts and techniques developed in the unit. The student also has to explain why his procedure did lead to a solution. Some of the problems are open-ended; some have a single well-defined answer. The problems are different from any the student has encountered in the unit. We believe that the student's performance on such problems gives good evidence of his understanding, initiative, and mastery of techniques for several reasons: (1) The novelty of the problems prevents them from being solved by recall of information: (2) The experimental nature of the problems requires student initiative and grasp of technique; (3) The verbal explanation of the procedures prevents a fortuitous mechanical solution that works only in a special case; and (4) Since the verbal explanation is accompanied by concrete operations, one can determine the extent to which the student can function consistently in both these modes.

In the remainder of this chapter we shall give two examples of evaluation studies that were carried out in 1965 and 1966. One of these was conducted by individual-interview techniques, while the other was done with entire classes and required the children to make written records of their responses.

SOLUTIONS APPRAISAL

The SCIS unit *Solutions* was taught in eleven trial classes between September 1964 and February 1965. There were four third-grade classes, two combined third and fourth grades, four fourth-grade classes, and one fifth-grade class. The teaching program in nine of the classes extended over approximately three months. Two classes deviated from this schedule. In one third grade the teaching program ranged over somewhat more than four months, and in one combined third-fourth grade it was accelerated to six weeks.

A brief quotation from the introduction to the *Solutions* unit will indicate its scope:

> The unit on *Solutions* is divided into two chapters. In the first chapter, "Making Solutions," the children gain experience with several water-soluble and insoluble substances. They observe the formation of solutions and destroy the solutions by letting the water evaporate. They also acquire ease in manipulating some laboratory apparatus and in keeping a record of their observations. In the second chapter, "Concentration," the pupils become concerned with the proportions of the two substances that make up the solution.

They also make solutions using liquids other than water. In the second chapter, the children's ability to follow printed laboratory instructions and to keep records is developed further.[8]

The concept *concentration* was "invented" for the children in the second chapter through concrete operational definitions having to do with the darkness of the colored solution and the amount of residue left when the water in a solution evaporated. The concept *solution* was not "invented" by means of a definition; instead, the teacher merely used the word in context.

The following objectives for the children reveal some of the purposes of the fifteen Activities in the unit:

1. To observe the dissolving process.
2. To interpret dissolving as evidence of interaction.
3. To recover dissolved material by evaporating a solution.
4. To compare soluble and insoluble substances.
5. To separate insoluble substances from water by filtration.
6. To comprehend the concentration concept.
7. To prepare solutions of differing concentrations.
8. To discover differences in concentration among solutions.
9. To work with liquids other than water.
10. To observe changes in concentration with time.
11. To use the student manual to record observations.
12. To use a medicine dropper as a tool.

To secure information about what the pupils learned, a set of ten observational and experimental problems was constructed and presented to the children in each trial class. Details of the procedure will be given shortly. The appraisal took place within a week after the completion of instruction in all classes except the accelerated one; the appraisal for that group occurred about two months after the completion of instruction. The performance by the children in that class was, nevertheless, about the same as that of the children in the other trial classes. For comparison purposes, a third- and a fifth-grade class which had not participated in the teaching program were also examined.

The experimental problems were mimeographed on separate pieces of paper, and each child was given a booklet with a random-ordered selection of five from the following ten problems:

[8] *Solutions*, Trial edition (Berkeley: Science Curriculum Improvement Study 1964), pp. 2–3.

Determining whether an unknown forms a solution

Experiment 1. Identify solutions by inspection [each child].
Experiment 2. Identify relative concentrations of copper chloride solutions by inspection [each child].
Experiment 3. Separate copper nitrate from sulfur.
Experiment 4. Separate sodium dichromate from copper oxide.
Experiment 5. Separate cobalt chloride from calcium carbonate.
[Each child did 3, 4, or 5.]
Experiment 6. Separate clear water from sandy water.
Experiment 7. Separate crystals from a solution of sodium chloride.
Experiment 8. Determine whether an unknown [sodium thiosulfate] dissolves in water.

Experiment 9. Determine whether an unknown [calcium carbonate] dissolves in water.

Experiment 10. Determine relative concentrations of four unknown solutions [sodium chloride in water].

[Each child did two problems from 6, 7, 8, 9, and 10, but not both 8 and 9.]

The samples to be used in each experiment were available at ten stations, numbered to correspond to the experiments. The children had access to all of the apparatus used in the unit, which included jars, funnels, filter paper, watch glasses, spoons, medicine droppers, vials, tea bags, paper clips, and a warming tray. Each child had a plastic tray to protect his desk.

The oral instructions given to the children were to write their names on each page, to do the experiments as they wished by securing any necessary equipment, to answer the questions on the page, to rip off and turn in the page, and to wash and return the equipment before starting the next experiment. Children were given assistance in reading the problems and in spelling, but were not assisted in deciding on a procedure. Any questions about procedure were answered encouragingly but noncommittally, e.g., "If that's what you want to do, go ahead." Children who turned in papers with a very sketchy explanation were asked to expand their statement or were permitted to dictate a brief statement to one of the adult supervisors. Children who claimed they did not know what to do were encouraged to state this and to proceed to their next experiment. The children in the comparison classes were introduced to the apparatus by name, but its function was not described or illustrated.

Most impressive to all observers was the efficiency and dispatch with which the children in the trial classes proceeded. With the exception of two or three children in each class, all trial classes completed their assignments in about sixty minutes of work. A few children finished much earlier and were given, at their own request, additional problems that had not been included in their booklets. The comparison fifth grade worked a little more slowly; the comparison third grade worked much more slowly.

Before making an analysis of the results, it may be worthwhile to analyze the children's tasks with regard to the following three components:

1. Reading and comprehending the problem statement. Whenever requested, an adult supervisor read the problem statement to a child. He did not give any explanation, however. There were approximately thirty requests for assistance in reading in each trial class out of a total of 150 papers being used. In the comparison third grade there were about 100 such requests; two supervisors were occupied almost full time with this work.

2. Deciding on a procedure to be followed and carrying it out. The supervisors gave no assistance here. Undoubtedly, there was some communication and imitation among the children. To minimize these factors, the problem pages were distributed in a scrambled order so only five or six children worked on a particular problem at one time.

3. Recording results, explanations, and/or procedure. Many children had difficulty describing what they had done and/or why they had done it. Supervisors frequently asked children to be more explicit, assisted with spelling, and occasionally added a note to clarify statements on the problem page after it was turned in. The children's greatest weakness lay in this area.

The appraisal was directed particularly at the children's ability to devise a procedure for solving their problem and to carry out this procedure. Since the children's own records were the major source of information about what they did, our analysis very likely underestimates their ability. We shall now describe six of the experimental problems in detail and survey the range of pupils' procedures in each. A value judgment about the adequacy or inadequacy of each behavior will also be indicated. The other four problems produced similar results and are omitted for the sake of brevity.

A total of 244 children participated in the appraisal of the 11 trial classes. The actual number of reported pages (including incomplete ones) that were collected for each experiment is indicated in the tables of data. Since each child did only five experiments selected from ten, there is not the same number of reports for all experiments. For experiment 1, data from twenty-one students in one class, which was given the questions in a very difficult and misleading form, were eliminated. No grade level differences in the trial classes were found. Because of the relatively small numbers of children, the data from classes were combined. The two comparison classes included forty-one children.

EXPERIMENT 1. IDENTIFY SOLUTIONS BY INSPECTION

Five systems in vials or jars were presented for observation, as follows:

System in vial 1A: copper sulfate (dissolved) and water.
System in vial 1B: calcium carbonate and water.
System in vial 1C: cooking oil and water.
System in vial 1D: sodium chloride (dissolved) and water.
System in vial 1E: copper oxide and water.

Instruction Sheet for the Children

Observe the five vials. Shake the vials if you like. Do not open the vials.

Is there a solution in vial 1A?   Yes   No   Can't tell
Is there a solution in vial 1B?   Yes   No   Can't tell
Is there a solution in vial 1C?   Yes   No   Can't tell
Is there a solution in vial 1D?   Yes   No   Can't tell
Is there a solution in vial 1E?   Yes   No   Can't tell
How did you know?   _____

Correct responses were: solutions in 1A, 1D; not solutions in 1B, 1C, and 1E. Actually, the system in 1D could have been pure water, but only very few children were concerned with this ambiguity. The children's procedure ("How did you know?") included looking at the systems (the vast majority), shaking them, noticing material at the bottom, noticing color, and noticing bubbles. The results for ten of the trial classes are given in Table 2.

TABLE 2

Children in Trial Classes

	A	B	C	D	E
Solution	194	97	66	113	115
Not a solution	17	104	125	71	74
Can't tell	11	21	32	34	32
No response	1	1	0	5	2
Total	223	223	223	223	223

Clearly, the copper sulfate solution was the easiest to identify, the two suspensions were the most difficult. Apparently, the relative homogeneity of the shaken-up suspensions caused them to be mistaken for solutions.

Actually, the data in Table 2 conceal quite interesting fluctuations from class to class. In other words, many class groups answered an item consistently one way or the other, but the combined responses were fairly equally divided. One way of presenting this feature is to tabulate "class consensus," defined as the choice of at least 60 per cent of the pupils in a class. If fewer than 60 per cent of the pupils agreed, the class consensus was "undecided" (see Table 3).

TABLE 3

Number of Trial Classes

	A	B	C	D	E
Solution	10	2	1	6	4
Not a solution	0	4	7	1	4
Undecided	0	4	2	3	2
Total	10	10	10	10	10

Four of the classes had a correct consensus on all five systems. One class considered all five systems to be solutions; one class was undecided on all systems except that in vial 1A. We conclude, therefore, that the teachers approached the solution concept in different ways and that the discussion of this topic in the teacher's manual is not adequate, but that third and fourth-grade children are capable of grasping and applying the distinction between systems which are not solutions and those which are.

In the comparison third grade, only five of the children recorded answers, the others did not know. In the comparison fifth grade, two children made correct choices for all five systems, and two children made five incorrect choices. The results are given in Table 4.

EXPERIMENT 3. SEPARATE COPPER NITRATE FROM SULFUR
EXPERIMENT 4. SEPARATE SODIUM DICHROMATE FROM COPPER OXIDE
EXPERIMENT 5. SEPARATE COBALT CHLORIDE FROM CALCIUM CARBONATE

These three experiments were similar in principle, but somewhat different in practice. The sulfur aggregated and floated when mixed with water, while copper oxide and calcium carbonate settled to the bottom much more slowly. A complete procedure of separation would include mixing the sample with water, filtering the mixture, and evaporating the filtrate to recover the dissolved material. Not many children reported the use of watch glasses to evaporate a sample of the solution. Here, the supervisors were able to check the completeness of the children's record keeping by making a count of the number of watch glasses left on the warming tray at the end of the period. It appeared that somewhat less than half of the children who carried out an evaporation stated this fact in their reports.

TABLE 4

Children in Comparison Classes

	A	B	C	D	E
Solution	16	15	12	5	9
Not a solution	2	3	5	9	6
Can't tell	1	0	0	4	3
No response	22	23	24	23	23
Total	41	41	41	41	41

Instructions for the Children (similar for #3, #4, and #5)

Take one package from Station 3. The package contains sulfur mixed with copper nitrate. Try to separate the sulfur and the copper nitrate. Use any other objects you need. DO NOT TASTE THE MIXTURE.

Did you separate sulfur?   Yes   No
Did you separate copper nitrate?   Yes   No
Tell about your experiment   _____

The children's judgment as to whether or not they had successfully separated the substances was quite subjective. Some, for example, mixed their unknown with water and then considered the substances separated, perhaps because the colored solution was visible and distinct from the undissolved component that settled to the bottom or floated on top. Others carried out the same operation and concluded that one or both of the substances had not been separated. In tallying the behavior, therefore, the "yes" or "no" answers were ignored, and only the report of the experiment was considered. One deficiency in the reports compared to actual performance has been mentioned. There were also other omissions in the descriptions. By encouraging the children to complete their

Separating a mixture of solid substances

reports and by themselves making notes on separate sheets, the supervisors hoped to obtain a fairly complete picture of the children's procedure. Table 5 presents the results of the appraisal in terms of seven behavioral alternatives. The entry "mechanical separation" refers to the pushing apart of the crystal grains by hand, with a pencil or with a pin.

TABLE 5

Number of Children

	Trial Classes				Comparison Classes
	Exp. 3	Exp. 4	Exp. 5	combined 3–4–5	combined 3–4–5
No report	8	7	10	25	13
Mechanical separation	2	2	2	6	6
Mixed with water *only*	19	16	18	53	15
Used tea bag to immerse sample in water	20	11	14	45	1
Mixed with water and filtered	39	44	39	122	4
Mixed with water and evaporated the clear liquid	1	8	3	12	1
Mixed with water, filtered, and evaporated the filtrate	4	7	3	14	1
Total number of reports	93	95	89	277[1]	41

[1]Some children who finished before the end of the hour carried out extra experiments. Hence, this number is greater than 244.

Quite a few children used a tea bag and then filtered; they are included under the latter category only. We should also like to add again that the last two categories are known to underestimate the children's performance, because we made an actual count of six to ten watch glasses with colored solutions on the warming trays after each class. By contrast, the comparison third grade left no watch glasses; the fifth grade left two. We conclude that the children in all classes developed good ideas about the separation of mixtures by dissolving and filtering (with tea bag or filter) even though the *Solutions* unit did not include any activity involving separation of two solid substances.

EXPERIMENT 7. SEPARATE THE CRYSTALS FROM A SOLUTION OF
SODIUM CHLORIDE

To make this problem more concrete, a package of sodium
chloride was displayed at the station from which the children
obtained the vial with the colorless solutions. The problem could
be solved by evaporating some of the liquid to obtain the crystal-
line residue.

Instructions for the Children

Take one vial from Station 7. The liquid in the vials is a
solution of crystals in water. Get some of the crystals from
the solution. Use any other objects you need. DO NOT
TASTE THE LIQUID.
Did you get some of the crystals?   Yes_____ No_____
Tell about your experiment _____

The children's procedures included evaporation of samples,
filtering, examining the liquid with a hand lens to find the crystals,
and helplessness (Table 6). Some children who filtered claimed to
have recovered crystals by this process.

TABLE 6

Number of Children

	Trial Classes	Comparison Classes
Evaporation	43	2
Filtering	43	1
Other procedure or none at all	24	13
Total number of reports	110	16

We conclude that the technique of evaporation was not well
understood by the children in the trial classes. This observation
raises serious questions about the children's concept of solution.
In one class, however, seven out of the ten children who did the
experiment used the evaporation procedure and none filtered.

EXPERIMENT 10. DETERMINE RELATIVE CONCENTRATION OF FOUR
SOLUTIONS

The comparison of the concentration of the four salt solutions could be carried out in two ways: Equal samples could be evaporated and the residue compared, or drops of solutions could be dropped into pure water and the schlieren compared. The liquid levels were made approximately equal to de-emphasize this variable. Other possible techniques were smelling (the rubber stoppers unfortunately left an odor on the vials) and shaking to watch the behavior of air bubbles mixed with the solution. After selecting a promising technique, the child had to apply it successfully. The drop test gave immediate results, but with the evaporation test most children were unable to report during the appraisal session. In one class, however, the children kept records of their watch glass numbers and submitted supplementary reports on the next day.

Instructions for the Children

Borrow a set of four vials from Station 10. The four vials contain solutions of a solid substance in water or pure water. Find out which solutions have a high concentration. Find out which solutions have a low concentration. Find out which liquids are pure water. Use any other objects you need. DO NOT TASTE THE LIQUIDS.
Solution with high concentration in vial _____ _____
Solution with low concentration in vial _____ _____
Pure water in vial _____ _____
Tell about your experiment _____

The children's reports were examined in two stages. First, their procedure was tabulated (Table 7); then the experimental results of those children who had used the evaporation or drop tests were compared with the actual concentration (Table 8). The results of children who used some other procedure were not tallied. In the comparison classes, no child used an acceptable procedure.

The children's work on Experiment 10 indicated that about one-third of the trial class children did indeed learn to carry out an effective testing procedure and that this is not part of their ordinary accomplishments. There was, however, considerable variation from class to class; In some classes most of the children were unable to find the concentrations; in others most of them were able to do so.

TABLE 7

Number of Children

	Trial Classes	Comparison Classes
Evaporation test	18 ⎱ 51	0 ⎱ 0
Dropper test	33 ⎰	0 ⎰
Looking, smelling, etc.	44	6
No procedure	15	7
Total number of reports	110	13

TABLE 8

Number of Completed Analyses[1]

	High Concentration	Low Concentration	Water
Correct identification	35	26	32
Incorrect identification	12	15	17
Total number reported	47	41	49

[1] Most analyses based on the evaporation test were not completed. With a few exceptions, the data in Table 8 represent the work of the thirty-three children who used the dropper test.

It is our conclusion from the entire appraisal that the *Solutions* unit did succeed in developing student initiative and mastery of certain experimental techniques. The students also seem to have acquired an understanding of concentration, but they seem not to have been able to distinguish solutions from suspensions. Indeed, as was pointed out at the beginning of this section, an operational definition of *concentration* was provided, but the same was not done for the concept *solution*. This failure would appear to have been an error by the authors of the unit.

In the present revision of the teaching program, a separate unit entitled *Solutions* is not planned. Instead, the activities are being included in *Interaction* (Grade 2), in *Subsystems* (Grade 3), and in units being planned for grades 4 and 5. By giving the children experience with dissolving and crystallization in earlier grades, we hope to prepare them for the solutions concept when that will be introduced in the upper grades.

VARIATION AND MEASUREMENT APPRAISAL

The SCIS unit *Variation and Measurement* was taught in seven second-grade classes and in one combined second-third grade during the fall of 1965. The teaching schedule in all eight classes extended over approximately four months. The following quotation from the introduction to the unit will indicate its scope:

As with the other units prepared by the Science Curriculum Improvement Study, the objective of VARIATION AND MEASUREMENT is to give the children a start in looking at objects and at groups of objects in a more analytical way...

Each of the first seven lessons of the first chapter entitled "Variation" presents an experience in making comparisons of certain characteristics of objects in a collection that the child can examine at his own desk. In lessons one and two, the comparison is qualitative; it concerns the shape and size of leaves. In lessons three through seven, the comparison is quantitative; it requires counting numbers of peas in a pod, beans in a pod, leaflets on a leaf, raisins in raisin bread, and colored specks on floor tiles. This operation may be called measurement in natural units. By pooling their observations, the children in one class can display their data as a histogram and can begin to recognize that the sample of fifty to a hundred specimen examined by them gives significant information about that kind of object as it occurs in nature. . . .

In the next three chapters of the unit the children explore the measurement of length, area, and volume in terms of arbitrary standards. These activities are more abstract than the measurement by means of natural units as was done in the first chapter. We should like to point out that we introduce independent standards of measurement in the three chapters. Ultimately, of course, the units of area and volume, the square foot and the cubic foot, are derived from the unit of length. At the first grade level, however, it is important that the children acquire an intuitive understanding of measurement with arbitrary units and of the rather abstract properties such as length, area, and volume that can be measured. Only when such an understanding has been established will the children be able to grasp the possible relationship among standards of measurement of the three different properties. . . .[9]

[9] *Variations and Measurement*, Trial Edition (Berkeley: Science Curriculum Improvement Study, 1964), pp. 5–6.

Even though the text of the teacher's manual does not contain explicit statements of objectives, one certainly might expect that children's ability to make quantitative comparisons of length, area, and volume would be improved by the learning experience. One might also expect that children would be able to display data as a histogram.

The appraisal to secure information about what the pupils learned was prepared in the light of these expectations. It consisted of two parts: In one part, each child in an entire class was given ten pieces of wood to make a histogram of the distribution of the number of growth rings on each piece; in the second part, single children were interviewed concerning a comparison of length, area, and volume of certain test objects. The individual interview technique was used in spite of its being very time-consuming so it would be possible to learn the children's reasoning that accompanied their measuring procedures. All the exercises were administered by an appraisal supervisor, not the children's regular teacher.

PART I

The population of objects in this exercise consisted of ten $1'' \times 2'' \times \frac{1}{4}''$ blocks of pine or maple, all of them with easily identified dark lines derived from the annual rings. Each child received a bag with the ten pieces of wood and a record sheet on which to record the number of lines and construct the histogram. A sample record sheet is reproduced in Figure 8. A class usually completed this work in about fifteen minutes. While the papers were being collected, the appraisal supervisor asked a few of the children three questions that required them to interpret the histogram. The results of the appraisal are given in Table 9. It is clear that most of the children were able to do the work very well and that more than half were even able to give verbal explanations.

PART II

In the individual interviews a total of over sixty children (thirty-one from SCIS trial classes, thirty-three or thirty-four from comparison classes in schools of a comparable socioeconomic level) were asked to make comparisons of length, area, and volume of the following test objects:

FIGURE 8
Data Sheet Used by Second Grader

Name _____Maryan_____ Bag Number _37_

4	4
6	5
4	5
5	5
5	5

Make a histogram of the numbers you found.

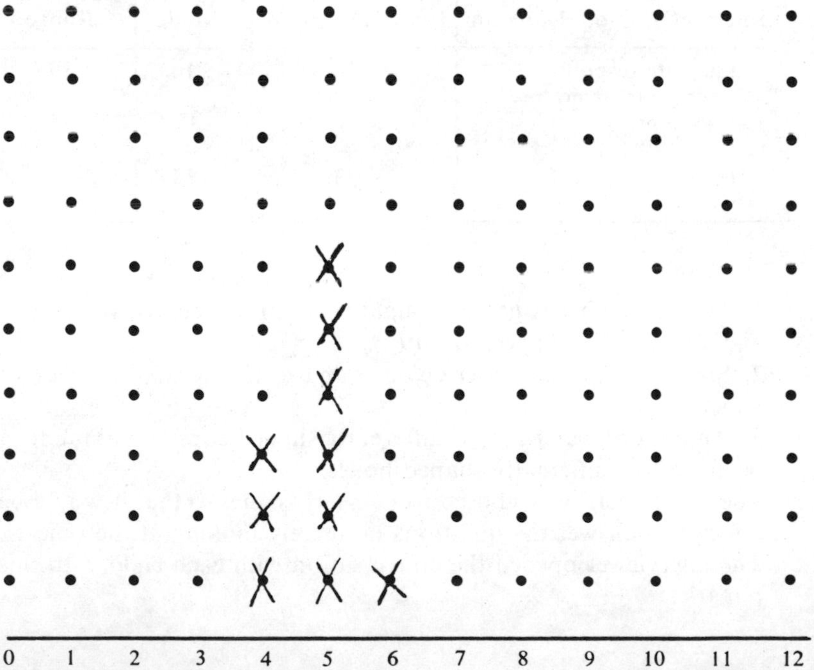

| 0 | 1 | 2 | 3 | 4 | 5 | 6 | 7 | 8 | 9 | 10 | 11 | 12 |

TABLE 9

Construction of Histograms

Response	Number of Children
Counting Lines	
counted grain lines	108
did not count lines	
adequately	7
Total	115
Constructing Histograms	
accurate histogram	76
histogram with 1 error	16
histogram with 2 errors	1
histogram with 3 or more	
errors	3
meaningless histogram	16
no response	3
Total	115

Interpretation of Histogram	Read Data from Histogram	Identified Mode	Identified Range
adequate response	26	16	19
inadequate or no			
response	7	17	14
Total	33	33	33

1. Length of a heavy gauge straight wire (10″), a curved wire (11″), and a corkscrew-shaped wire (9″).

2. Size of a square- , a circular- , and a kidney-shaped piece of paper.

3. Amount of water in two differently shaped cups and amount of beans in two differently shaped boxes.

The test objects were chosen to be nearly equal so that it would be difficult to answer the questions by merely looking at the objects. The interviewer opened the conversation with each child with this remark:

I have brought some measuring puzzles for you to figure out. You can do some experiments to figure them out, or you can tell me what you think. I have a box here with different tools or objects you can use to do your experiments with. You can look for what you need, or you can ask me for it. If I don't have exactly what you want, maybe I have something like it.

This introduction was intended to encourage the children to take initiative in solving the problems, to devise procedures, and not to give only minimal verbal answers to the questions being asked.

To illustrate the procedure, some of the precise questions and a survey of the children's verbal and manipulative responses will be given for those readers interested in the details. The reader will notice that the questions do not use the words *length, area*, and *volume*. Instead, words like *size* and *amount* are employed. There are two reasons for this decision: First, it was expected that children from comparison classes might not be familiar with the words; second, it was thought that the meaning of *size* and *amount* (i.e., whether they meant length, area, or volume) would be inferred from the context and that the children's ability to make the appropriate interpretation might have been influenced by the teaching program.

Here we point out the general conclusions. On many of the measurement tasks the children from trial classes and from comparison classes did not perform very differently. In other words, the measurement skills tested in the interviews were not communicated by the *Variation and Measurement* teaching program any differently than they were communicated to the children through other school and home activities. There was a very noticeable qualitative difference between the two groups, however, in that the children from SCIS trial classes were much more cautious than the others in committing themselves to an answer on the basis of merely looking at the test objects. Many refused to answer questions without making some kind of actual measurement or other manipulative comparison. The children from trial classes were also more cautious in their estimate of measurements, frequently repeating an operation in order to verify its result.

1. *Linear Measurement—Comparison of Straight and Curved Wire*

   Question A. Here is the first puzzle. Can you tell me just by looking whether the straight wire is longer or shorter, or whether it is the same size as the bent wire? Or do you need to do something to find out?

Question B. How can you be sure? What could you do to prove that the straight one is [whatever the child said] compared to the bent one?

Question C. Here is a piece of wire which is easy to bend and which is just as long as the straight wire. Could you use this wire to find out which is longer? [Child is given a thin copper wire of the same length as the straight heavy gauge wire.]

Question D. Suppose we didn't have a wire which was just the same size as the straight wire. Could you use a wire that was a lot longer to measure the two wires? [Child is given a longer piece of thin copper wire.]

Question E. Suppose we had only a tiny piece of wire like this. Could you use this to find out which was longer? [Child is given a short piece of copper wire, about one and a half inches in length.]

The children's responses to these questions are given in Table 10.

TABLE 10

Measurement of Length (Straight Wire vs. Curved Wire)

Response	Number of Children Responding					
	SCIS Trial Classes (31)			Comparison Classes (34)		
Question A						
Straight is longer	4			12		
Equal length	5			9		
Bent is longer	8			6		
Refuse verbal answer without measurement	14			6		
No response	0			1		
Question B						
Unbend the bent wire	20			24		
Measure with a tape	7			2		
No response	4			8		
Question C, D, and E	C	D	E	C	D	E
Able	28	20	9	26	18	5
Unable	3	11	22	8	16	29

The most significant finding is that almost half of the SCIS trial class pupils refused to answer Question A until they were permitted to make a measurement. Also noteworthy is that Question E (use of the short wire) could not be answered by most children.

2. *Area Measurement—Comparison of Blue Circular and Square Papers (with the circle's diameter a little larger than the edge of the square) Placed on a Gray Rectangular Background*

Question A. Here are two playgrounds. [Indicate gray background.] A round wading pool was built in this playground

Measuring the area of lakes using beans

for the children to wade and swim in. And a square wading pool was built in this playground nearby. Can you tell just by looking whether the two wading pools are the same size, or whether one has more room to wade or less room to wade than the other? Or do you need to do something to find out?

Question B. How can you be sure this one is [whatever the child said] than that one? What could you do to be sure?

Question C. Could you use these beans [kidney beans] to find out how much [whatever the child said] it is?

Question D. I have here a piece of plastic that has many little squares on it. [A one centimeter grid was painted on a sheet of flexible, transparent plastic.] They are all the same size. Could you use this to tell how much [whatever the child said] it is?

The children's responses to these questions are given in Table 10. It should be pointed out that lima beans had been used for area measurement in *Variation and Measurement* and that the square grid, an optional activity, had been used in one SCIS trial class with seven children in the sample. The ambiguity of the word *size* which was used in the question became evident from the children's responses. They interpreted it to mean area, perimeter, or diameter, as can be seen from Table 11.

To interpret Question B, one must have additional information about the children's intention in putting the circle on the square to demonstrate the size difference. Some made remarks such as, "The circle is wider," or, "The corners of the square are extra," which indicate their thinking. Through such clues, it was possible to assign many of the responses into categories of area, perimeter, and diameter comparison. The other responses can be assigned to these categories quite unambiguously. The result of this analysis is shown in Table 12. Questions C and D revealed two things about the trial teaching program: The children did learn to use beans as units of measurement, but they did not learn to prefer area over perimeter as criterion of size in a wading pool.

3. *Amount of Liquid in Two Differently Shaped Cups (One Wide and Shallow, one Narrow, Tall, and Flared)*

Question A. Here we have two cups of water. Can you tell me just by looking whether they have the same amount of water, or whether one cup has more or less water in it?

Question B. What could you do to be sure? What could you do to prove to me that this cup has [whatever the child said] water in it than that one?

Question C. Could you use this cup, which is just the same size as your tall cup, to make sure? [Child is given the cup.]

Question D. Suppose you had only a very small cup like this. Could you use this cup to make sure which of the cups has more water in it? [Child is given a one-ounce tapered cup.]

TABLE 11

Measurement of Area (Square vs. Circle)

Response	Number of Children Responding	
	SCIS Trial Classes (31)	Comparison Classes (33)
Question A		
Square larger	22	23
Equal	0	3
Circle larger	2	4
Refuse verbal answer without measurement	7	3
No response	0	0
Question B		
Put circle on top of square	11	17
Use beans to cover shapes	1	0
Cut the circle to fit square	1	2
Measure around edge	7	2
Measure diameters	5	1
No response	3	11
Question C		
Use beans to cover shapes	18	8
Use beans around edge of shapes	12	7
Use beans across shapes	1	5
No response	0	13
Question D		
Count squares all over shapes	18	12
Count squares around edge of shapes	7	6
Count squares across shapes	2	3
No response	4	12

74852

TABLE 12

Comparison of Square and Circle (Question B)

	Number of Children Responding	
Category of Response	SCIS Trial Classes (31)	Comparison Classes (33)
Area	12	7
Perimeter	10	4
Diameter	6	6
Unknown	0	5
No response	3	11

The children's responses are given in Table 13. Clearly, the differences in responses of the two groups of children are quite small and insignificant in a sample of this size. It is interesting that Question D was the most difficult of all the questions in the interview. To make comparison of the amounts of water with the very small measuring cup, this cup has to be filled repeatedly and then emptied into an extra container so that the water which has been measured is separated from the water which has not been measured. The task is analogous to the one requiring repeated application of a small piece of wire, Question 1E. That task also proved difficult for all the children, but not quite as hard as Question 3D. The use of beans in Question 2C, in principle the same problem of repeated use of a unit of measurement, was not nearly as troublesome. A small follow-up study was therefore carried out in which twenty-two children were asked to compare amounts of water in two containers, first with one small measuring cup, then with many identical ones, then with a single one again, in close succession. The results are shown in Table 14. The use of many cups appears to be much easier, and three children learned to use the single cup from the one experience with many cups.

Several suggestions for revision of *Variation and Measurement* can be derived from the appraisal study that has been described:

1. Include experiences with the repeated use of a unit of measurement.

2. Include some experiences of displacement and deformation of objects (bending of wires, matching of flat shapes, pouring of

TABLE 13

Water in a Tall and in a Low Cup

Response	Number of Children Responding	
	SCIS Trial Classes (31)	Comparison Classes (33)
Question A		
Tall has more	6	12
Equal	4	11
Low has more	12	7
Refuses verbal answer without measurement	9	3
No response	0	0
Question B		
Uses an additional (matching) cup and pours	15	12
Uses two matching cups	2	1
Describes shape of water (2 dimensions)	4	2
Describes height of water	1	6
Describes width of water	2	1
Describes circumference of water	1	0
Looks	1	1
No response	5	10

Questions C and D	C	D	C	D
Able to do it	25	3	23	4
Unable to do it	6	28	10	29

TABLE 14

Use of a Small Measuring Cup

Response	Number of Children (22)		
	Small Cup	Many Cups	Single Cup
Able to use cup or cups	2	16	5
Unable to use cup or cups	20	6	17

liquids) to investigate conservation of length, area, and volume under these transformations.

3. Introduce more clearly the distinction between diameter, perimeter, and area of a figure.

In concluding this account, we should like to add two anecdotes that give evidence of originality on the children's part. To compare the length of the straight and curved lines (Question 1A), one girl sang a little song while she was gliding her finger along each wire. The longer wire, she explained, was the one that permitted her to sing more of the song. To compare the number of beans in two differently shaped boxes (a problem not described in detail here), a boy poured the beans into two equal tin cans and then floated the cans in the water pitcher used for the water in Problem 3. He concluded that the can which sank deeper into the water contained more beans. We hope that these two examples will indicate how rewarding the administering of a divergent evaluation problem can be.

PROBLEMS FOR FURTHER STUDY

The two evaluation examples that have been described reveal both the interesting possibilities of studying children's behavior and the difficulty of securing an unambiguous diagnosis of the strengths and weaknesses of a teaching unit.

One particular problem, already mentioned in connection with the *Variation and Measurement* interviews, has to do with the phrasing of the question or directions. On the one hand, certain scientific vocabulary is introduced in the SCIS units to make communication with the children more clear and powerful. One might, therefore, consider this vocabulary growth to be an integral part of the objectives and phrase questions accordingly. An evaluation would then consist of certain problems addressed to children from SCIS trial classes and the same problems, paraphrased in everyday language, addressed to children from comparison classes.

A second problem arises from the sequential nature of the SCIS program. Work in one unit frequently sets a stage for a later unit, as was described in the plans for revision of the *Solutions* unit. With the *Solutions* teaching program to be distributed over three or four years, it will be difficult to pinpoint the cause of learning problems that may be revealed in future evaluation activities. If a weakness is found, it may be in the unit where the solutions concept is introduced, or it may be in the preparatory activities in the earlier units.

It has also been found that the ideas of one unit are followed up and established more firmly in later units. An evaluation of *Systems*, for example, has shown that the children's only partial understanding of the systems concept at the conclusion of *systems* develops further during their work in *Interaction*. It therefore, may not be necessary or desirable to revise *Systems* to achieve a more complete understanding of the systems concept as a result of that unit alone.

A third problem, which was briefly mentioned in the review of the *Solutions* appraisal, is the variation in the teacher's approach from class to class. When the entire class is tested, as was the case in *Solutions*, consistent patterns of responses within one class may be contrasted with the patterns in another class. If the sample is small, such as the six or seven children from a class that were interviewed in the *Variation and Measurement* appraisal, it is not possible to identify these effects.

We hope that the reader will be stimulated to consider some of these problems and perhaps carry out investigations that will clarify the issues. After all, evaluation is important for everyone concerned with education, even though the role it plays and the emphasis it is given will vary for the teacher who is planning lessons, the school administrator who selects an instructional program, and the curriculum-maker who designs procedures that teachers can use and from which children can learn.

VII

SCIS and The Schools

EXPANDING SCIS'S INTERACTION WITH THE PUBLIC SCHOOLS

The construction and trial of SCIS science units in the Berkeley area test schools, as described in Chapter I, give considerable information about the units' usability by teachers. These teachers work closely with Study staff members, and all equipment and materials are provided directly by the Study. Based on the information obtained from the Berkeley trials and the developing conceptual point of view of the project, the materials are then revised and prepared for production as a preliminary commercial version of the SCIS program. This is needed to bridge the gap between the research and development use of the materials in Berkeley and their eventual use in the normal elementary school situation. As part of the commercial version, an integrated package containing both the kit of equipment and supplies and the printed materials for teacher and pupils will be produced. Kits for the individual units will be available commercially to school districts that wish to carry out experimentation with and evaluation of the materials.

About seventy classes at each grade level will be part of the formal SCIS Trial Center Program. Communication will be established with those additional school districts trying the materials so that SCIS and future revisions can benefit from the schools' experiences. For the district, this will provide an opportunity for receiving answers to questions about the program.

Testing, to take place both in the SCIS Trial Centers and in the other school districts that take advantage of the opportunity, will help to reveal the strengths, weaknesses, and opportunities for improvement which exist in the materials. Information obtained from teachers not closely associated with the SCIS staff and from the trial of the units with children of a broader spectrum of socio-economic backgrounds than have been available to the Study in the Berkeley area will provide valuable information necessary before the development of a final version of the materials can be undertaken. The major source of feedback to the Study about the operation of the preliminary commercial version will come from the five trial centers established by the project. It is expected that the information obtained from the other districts also will be valuable to the further development of SCIS materials.

THE TRIAL CENTERS

SCIS Trial Centers have been established at the University of California at Los Angeles, the University of Hawaii, Michigan State University, the University of Oklahoma, and Teachers College, Columbia University. Three or four elementary schools in the geographic area of each center except Michigan State began using SCIS materials in the fall of 1966. Teaching in the Michigan State Center will begin in the fall of 1967. In the first year only the first grade is included in the experiment. As the children in the experimental groups advance a grade level, the additional material for this level will be produced and supplied until the entire K-6 curriculum in preliminary form is tested. All materials for use in the trial centers will be produced commercially as described in this chapter.

The five trial centers are organized in a fashion similar to one another. Each of the centers is supervised by a locally appointed coordinator who is responsible for conducting inservice education programs, coordinating evaluation activities, disseminating materials, and collecting feedback. During the semester prior to their involvement in the program, the teachers associated with the trial center will participate in an inservice education course on the structure, methods, and philosophy of the SCIS curriculum. There is also an orientation conference for the participating teachers before the introduction of the new commercial materials in the fall of each year. Finally, there is an evaluation conference near the end of the year at which teachers can describe their experience and express their views in the presence of a staff member from the project headquarters in Berkeley. During the academic year, the center coordinator arranges for discussions, planning, and laboratory sessions as part of the continuing inservice education schedule. For their own education, the center coordinators make regular visits to Berkeley to observe the operation of the local laboratory schools and to remain in touch with the progress and orientation of SCIS. They also personally inform the SCIS staff of the progress taking place in the centers.

The trial centers serve as an experimental facility for SCIS and the cooperating institutions in four distinct but complementary ways. First, as already mentioned, the additional experience with the use of the materials by a larger group of teachers and pupils will test the reliability of the procedures and the devices for communicating with the teachers and pupils. Second, the work with the teachers in the trial centers not only makes possible their more effective participation, but it also serves as pilot experience for the development of an inservice education program to accompany the SCIS curriculum. Third, a sociological and psychological evaluation program of the trial experience will be carried out at the centers. Fourth, each of the cooperating institutions is associating the local trial center with its own educational activities in an appropriate way.

As an example of the fourth point, Michigan State, Teachers College and UCLA will use the trial center as a source of raw materials for graduate seminars, discussions, and doctoral dissertations in science education. The University of Oklahoma and the University of Hawaii, being primarily concerned with preservice and inservice teacher education, will use the program in their already established laboratory schools and demonstration facilities. This will give teachers and administrators both in training and in the field the opportunity to observe and study similarities and differences between a conventional science program and the SCIS program and to analyze many differences, including the especially significant ones in the SCIS approach to teaching and the role of the learner in the classroom.

The next sections of this chapter will explore in depth the plans for teacher education and evaluation just mentioned in relation to the functions of the centers.

TEACHER EDUCATION

The ultimate objectives of the SCIS program are modified capacities, understandings, and behaviors of the pupils leaving elementary school. It is most important to recognize that there are implicit in these certain behavioral objectives for the teachers. As the classroom use of SCIS materials continues, it is and will be possible to see how the curriculum materials should be adjusted and how they must be supplemented by an inservice teacher education program. Some of the more significant problem areas involved in the development of a teacher education program are: (1) Teachers' unfamiliarity with the phenomena under study in the units; (2) teachers' tendency to pursue convergent rather than divergent lines of questioning; (3) teachers' difficulty in dealing with logical or conceptual structures in science; and (4) teachers' lack of acquaintance with and experience in observing children's development during the stage of concrete mental operations.

To deal with these four problem areas and any others that may be discovered through experience, an inservice teacher education program is being developed under the leadership of Willard Jacobson, Professor of Natural Science at Teachers College, Columbia University. It will help and support the teachers in the SCIS trial centers who are to use the SCIS elementary science materials. Like the elementary science program, the inservice teacher education program is also experimental in nature, and it will also be revised and improved in light of experience. Eventually, it is expected that the teacher education materials that are under development will have general usefulness to school districts interested in adopting all or parts of the SCIS program.

The most important goal of the inservice education program is to aid the teachers who are involved to become better teachers. This is a worthy goal in itself, but it is essential for a useful trial of SCIS materials and procedures. To teach the SCIS program effectively, the teacher working in science should have the confidence to venture into new areas and try new approaches with children, should have sufficient background understanding of science and the SCIS program to move with children along divergent as contrasted to the more usual paths, and should have the sensitivity and insight to recognize the possible importance of various responses of children. These abilities cannot be developed overnight or over a semester;

instead, these are areas of development in which everyone concerned with teaching should continue to grow throughout his career. The inservice program should be a part of a continuing education in which participants grow in their effectiveness in working with children in science and other areas of the curriculum.

In a laboratory session, teachers observe and compute the period of horizontal oscillators

For the development of the teacher education program, procedures are being used which are similar to those that have been used in the growth of other aspects of the SCIS program. Utilization will also be made of the seminars and other resources of the associated teacher education institutions at the five trial centers.

During the semester that precedes the introduction of SCIS materials into the trial center classrooms, an inservice course is given to the individual teachers. The inservice work will be continued at least during the year the teachers first introduce the materials. For example, during spring and Summer 1966, the teachers who began teaching *Material Objects* in the fall of 1966 participated in such a course. The course serves largely as an introduction to the SCIS program, its philosophy and approach, and to a lesser extent as a general course in elementary school science. This part of the inservice program is structured to a considerable extent. In contrast, the ongoing inservice course during the time the SCIS materials are being tried will be of a very flexible nature and will be based on the needs and interests that develop among the teachers as they work with the children and the SCIS materials.

The inservice course prior to the introduction of SCIS materials undertakes the following kinds of activities:

1. The development of an understanding of the theoretical foundations of the SCIS approach. Certainly, if teachers are to use the SCIS materials to their full potentialities they will need to know something about the relationship of the SCIS program to the nature and structure of science and to the growth and development of children. The theoretical foundations of the SCIS project are studied through readings, discussions, listening to recordings, observing and analyzing films of SCIS classrooms, and laboratory-demonstration teaching.

2. The presentation through readings and discussions of a picture of how SCIS fits into the historical development of elementary science. The emphasis is placed on the evolutionary rather than revolutionary nature of change in the field.

3. The orientation of teachers to ways of working with children that are of special importance in this program. As an example, for an effective trial of many of the SCIS materials, it is essential that the children have laboratory-type experiences. This means that the classroom must be organized in a different way than many teachers have previously organized their rooms for science. Also, it is important that the teacher's mode of questioning be at least partially divergent, not the more usual convergent mode, i.e., the questions should lead children into further exploration of the phenomena of science that are being studied. It is suggested that the orientation of teachers to ways of working with children be through demonstration teaching, laboratory work, discussions, and films produced especially for this purpose.

These films are intended to present as normal as possible a classroom situation using SCIS materials. The films are made with a single portable camera and sound recorder with little editing done. After viewing the films, the teacher can analyze the techniques used and discuss the successes and problems found in this or any other lesson. Through such analysis the teacher in the inservice course can be helped to rethink her own approaches to science in the classroom and to restructure her role as a teacher when she uses SCIS

Kindergarten children sort beans

materials. For example, films which show "invention" and "discovery" lessons can be contrasted to help the teacher understand the differences in classroom organization and approach needed when working with these two very dissimilar aspects of the science program.

4. The orientation of teachers to the research and development aspects of the trial of SCIS materials and to their role in it is important. The teachers involved in the trial centers have an opportunity to make an important contribution to education. However, this will involve certain necessary changes in their classrooms and a certain amount of sensitivity to children's reactions and possible flaws in materials. Also, it will mean that there will be observers in the classrooms, evaluations to be made, and reports to be rendered. It is important that all teachers recognize the place and necessity of the research and development aspects of the program and the nature of the contribution that they are making as members of a research and development team.

5. The involvement of the teachers in professionalized science experiences that are closely related to the program and that will help to develop a better understanding of the nature and structure of the program. These professionalized science experiences are one of the most important features of the inservice course. A wide variety of teaching procedures are used such as laboratory work, teacher and student demonstrations, lectures, discussions, field experiences, and projects. Considerable time is devoted to laboratory work. For example, teachers become involved in the examination and study of mealworms when a dish of cereal containing mealworms is placed before them at an orientation session. Another example deals with solutions, the solution of solids and liquids, and the conservation of matter. A third example, which is presented in the next section in detail, is the study of sorting and grouping by properties using a collection of pieces of sandpaper of assorted grits cut into different sizes.

CLASSIFICATION AND SERIAL ORDERING:
AN EXAMPLE OF A PROFESSIONALIZED SCIENCE EXPERIENCE FOR TEACHERS
(adapted from the SCIS Teacher Training Program)

Classification and serial ordering are operations that are important in many areas of science. Both classification and serial ordering are operations that young children often delight in carrying out, and these experiences are an important foundation for other activities in the study of science.

Classification is the assigning of objects to groups on some accepted basis. In the science of biology, for example, living organisms are classified into the plant kingdom or the animal kingdom. Within these large groups, plants or animals can be classified into smaller subgroups: Animals can be further classified on the basis of whether or not they have a backbone. The most common, and the most useful, systems of classification in the sciences are based on the physical properties of objects. It is partially for this reason that considerable emphasis is placed upon the observation and description of the physical properties of objects early in the SCIS elementary science program.

Serial ordering is the arranging of objects in order on the basis of some property. In one of the most famous examples of serial ordering in science, various chemical elements were arranged in order of their weights. When elements were arranged in this way, it was noticed that certain chemical properties appeared periodically in the list. Based on these observations, Mendelyeev invented the Periodic Table of the Elements that has been of such value in the science of chemistry. In elementary school science, children can be encouraged to exercise their ingenuity in ordering various objects on the basis of a wide variety of properties and to state the basis on which the materials are serially ordered.

Various systems of classification and ordering can be conceived. The choice of which one is used is based on usefulness. In science, systems of classification and ordering founded on physical properties are usually the most beneficial. However, in some cases a system using geographical location or some other basis may be chosen. In most cases it is important to choose classification and ordering systems into which all objects that are being considered can fit. If some object, for example, does not have the property on which a particular classification or ordering system is based, the system is not very useful. As children continue to work in science, they should gain experience in deciding which is the most practical of several possible systems of classification and ordering.

In this laboratory exercise materials are provided that can be classified and ordered in many different ways. The teachers are asked to identify and use some of these ways.

Experiment 1. Yes-No (Binary) Classification. A simple, but very useful, system of classification is what may be called a "Yes-No" system. Objects either have a certain characteristic or they do not. For example, objects either have one round surface or they do not. The objects that have a round surface can be placed in one group and those that do not in another. This system is in common use in branches of the biological sciences. For example, animals either have a backbone or they do not.

In this experiment the teacher is given five pieces of sandpaper that have a variety of properties. These pieces of sandpaper are numbered on the back. Piece #1 is round, paper-backed, with a black fine grit surface; piece #2 is rectangular, paper-backed, with a tan very fine grit surface; piece #3 is a right triangle, paper-backed sample of rough grit sandpaper. The grit surface is tan and lighter than in #2. Piece #4 is an equilateral triangle made of emery cloth of a medium fine grit. The grit surface is black. Piece #5 is a square made of emery cloth of medium grit. The grit surface is black and rougher than in #4.

The teacher is asked to find as many properties as possible by which these pieces of sandpaper can be grouped into two sets. For example, the pieces can be grouped on the basis of whether they are black or not.

In the table below, one writes in the left-hand column (Property Column) as many properties as possible on the basis of which the pieces of sandpaper can be grouped. In the second column (Yes Column) one writes the numbers of the pieces of sandpaper that have this property. In the third column (No Column) one writes the numbers of the pieces of sandpaper that do not have this property.

Property	Yes	No
Ex. 1. Black color	1, 4, 5	2, 3
2. —	—	—
3. —	—	—

The experiment just described is the first one in the series on Classification and Serial Ordering. Other experiments in the group are: (1) Developing a classification scheme using fourteen pieces of sandpaper of assorted sizes, shapes, and grits; (2) serial ordering of objects on the basis of a given property using a collection of cork stoppers; and (3) suggesting possible interrelationships between objects that have been serially ordered. The corks and stoppers used in Experiments 2 and 3 are of various sizes and have been modified by boring holes of different sizes into them and painting them in different shades of red.

Through activities such as this, the teacher has experiences on an adult level which are directly related to the kinds of operations her children will be expected to carry out in the classroom when working with the *Material Objects* unit.

EVALUATION

Chapter VI took a first look at the evaluation procedures under way and being developed for the purpose of determining what children have learned from a teaching unit. This information is needed to guide the further development and revision of the SCIS program. In this section, no attempt is made to describe a definitive and absolute measurement of the scientific literacy of the pupils emerging from the SCIS program. Instead, concern is focused on assessing the impact of the program in such a way that teachers and curriculum designers can choose better strategies for teaching. In other words, the concern is with establishing feedback loops to analyze the experience in the classroom of teacher and pupil in order to help the teacher use this information in her future planning for the science program.

It is further useful to distinguish two kinds of feedback loops. The first one includes the curriculum project, the school, the teacher, and the pupils. The agency sensitive to the feedback information is the curriculum project, which must be prepared to modify the curriculum materials in the light of the classroom experience and which must have diagnostic devices that not only identify sources of difficulty but also provide some clue as to remedy. When the "final" edition of the project material is released, this feedback loop ceases to exist. The second kind of feedback loop includes the teacher and the pupils in the class. The teacher must be sensitive to the behavior of the students and to the behavior of the phenomena and must be prepared to change the classroom strategy in the light of this information. The teacher too, must have diagnostic devices—some even operating on the intuitive level—that identify both sources of difficulty and opportunities for achieving insight. These feedback loops must be permanently built into the curriculum and the teachers.

The construction of valid, reliable, and practical procedures that can be used routinely by the teacher for assessing student progress and that provide adequate data for studying the interaction of instructional and student variables is of central concern in this aspect of the evaluation program. In addition, the developmental nature of the SCIS curriculum creates an obligation to study the cumulative impact of the proposed program on the students, on the teachers, and on the total learning situation provided for students.

With these aims for evaluation, comparisons between students who have had the experimental program and those who have not are of secondary importance. It is, however, important to make comparisons among students within the program. Since all students in the program are unlikely to achieve the goals and objectives of the program to the same degree, information is needed to understand the complex of variables that is associated with differences in achievement of students. This kind of information is of value in improving the teaching-learning situation. At present it is impossible to identify all of the evaluation devices that will be needed in the program, but it is possible to mention some tasks that need to be accomplished. These are listed next.

The first task of any evaluation program is to name and define operationally *all* of the objectives of the curriculum. This step requires cooperative effort on the part of the designers of the curriculum materials, the classroom teachers, and the evaluators. Attention should be given not only to identifying and defining behavioral outcomes for the student, but also to possible effects that the program might have on teacher behavior and on the total learning environment provided for the students. The developmental nature of the curriculum needs to be considered and reflected in the definition of objectives.

The second is to devise methods of assessing progress toward the achievement of the various objectives. Since the program begins at the kindergarten-first grade level and since the objectives of the program are complex and varied, one cannot rely on paper-pencil devices. A good deal of ingenuity must be exercised to construct devices that will provide valid and reliable evidence of the achievement of *all* objectives. Appropriate methods of obtaining data on both cognitive and affective behavior of students, both within grades and across grades, must be developed. Since the teacher will be the ultimate user of these devices, the instruments developed must be not only valid and reliable but also practical to use in the classroom setting. This part of the program will require field trial of the methods as a part of their development.

A third is to identify the student, teacher, and school variables that are likely to help in the interpretation and use of the results of evaluation of student achievement in the curriculum. For the student the important variables are likely to be scholastic aptitude, socioeconomic status, family background, and previous experience. For the teacher, they are probably educational and experience background, attitude toward the program, and preparation for teaching the special curriculum. The school variables that we would be most interested in are organization for instruction, consultant services, per pupil expenditure, and innovative enterprise of the school district.

A fourth major task is the analysis and interpretation of data as they are obtained.

A fifth is the inservice education of classroom teachers in evaluation. The classroom teacher is the central figure in effective evaluation and in the constructive use of evaluation results. She must be able to assess student progress in order to make adjustments in the teaching-learning situation. Generally speaking, teachers are usually weak in evaluation techniques, and if they are not given systematic help they are likely to neglect this aspect when the present project is completed. Clearly the interaction between the inservice and evaluation programs will extend beyond the point made in this paragraph. For instance, the developmental nature of the curriculum and its cumulative impact are related to the conceptual structure that will be one basis of teacher education. Conversely, the effectiveness of the teacher education program will be reflected in the teacher behavior and ultimately the student behavior that are subjects of the evaluation study.

Some of the problems and opportunities which exist in the development of this evaluation aspect of the program, especially in regard to the primary grades, are listed here. Each of the seven items have implications for both of the feedback loops described earlier. Items 1, 2, 3, 6, and 7 are particularly applicable to the problem of providing feedback to the project from the schools, teachers, and pupils. This information will be used in the modification and improvement of the program itself. Items 4 and 5 are especially related to the long-term problems of providing the teacher with effective procedures for analyzing, interpreting, and evaluating the behavior of children in the class. This analysis is necessary not only to reinforce the teacher's belief in what she is doing, but is also the basis for continual development of the curriculum by the individual teacher in relation to the learning opportunities and problems found in the classroom.

1. Evaluation of students in the first and second grades requires the use of nonreading and nonwriting stimulus materials; therefore, visual materials and orally presented stimuli must be used. Since students at these grade levels have limited or nonexistent writing skills, much of the data will have to be collected individually rather than in groups. For example developing the ability to sort objects by properties is an objective of the first-grade program. To evaluate the children's ability to do this, they are presented with a tray

containing the following seven objects: a small black opaque marble, a thin transparent round plastic disc, a ball of red clay, a red checker (rough surface), a large red-and-white-striped marble, a square red block, and a round red bead with a hole in it. The child is asked to remove one object and then tell how the other six are alike according to some property. He is asked to do this as many times as he can, removing a different object each time. The evaluator records the number of different possibilities the child can find and also the property given. It is possible to remove each of the seven objects while grouping the other six by some characteristic. For example, if you remove the black marble, all the other objects are red.

2. Since the proposed curriculum is very new, there are no existing evaluation devices that are available for use. Entirely new materials have to be developed.

3. To obtain longitudinal data on the impact of the curriculum, comparable data must be collected over the full range of grades in which the curriculum is to be used. It is also necessary to start the development of evaluation materials at least a year in advance of the actual use of the curriculum in a particular grade.

4. Since the curriculum is new and little or no data exist on the levels of achievement to be expected of students at different stages, these must be developed. This is important because teachers tend to become insecure about their effectiveness in new curriculum areas and need some kind of reference point in framing their objectives.

5. If the classroom teacher is to be helped in assessing her students, then the procedures developed must be practical in the actual classroom setting. This will require experimenting with different methods of structuring the evaluation setting and recording results.

6. Evaluation of affective behaviors, such as attitudes, are much more difficult than evaluation of the cognitive behaviors; however, the effective component cannot be ignored. There has been relatively little work done on the evaluation of affective behaviors of young children; therefore this area will require considerable experimentation and field trials with different approaches to evaluation.

7. An effective evaluation program must be viewed as a continuous process and as an integral part of the total teaching-learning situation. Results of evaluation must be fed back promptly

to teachers, students, curriculum designers, and inservice education supervisors. This means that provisions must be made for processing data rapidly.

Some of the preparation and field trials of the evaluation program are taking place in Berkeley schools that are using SCIS materials and are on a schedule about three years ahead of teaching in the trial centers.

As was the case with the inservice program, it is expected that the evaluation program will make contributions beyond the needs of SCIS. For example, evidence will undoubtedly be obtained on the longitudinal development of affective and cognitive attributes of children in the elementary school.

THE PRELIMINARY PUBLICATION PROGRAM

The success of the teacher education and evaluation program just described is dependent on the more widespread use of SCIS materials so that sufficient numbers of teachers and pupils are involved in the tryout of the program. To accomplish this, the project has entered into an agreement with D. C. Heath and Company, Boston, Mass. to produce and market a preliminary commercial version of the project's materials. In cooperation with equipment and materials producers who will be chosen for the various separate SCIS units, an integrated package consisting of both the printed materials and classroom laboratory equipment and materials for all the children will be produced. For example, the kit for *Material Objects*, the first-grade unit produced in the preliminary publication program, includes all the objects needed to teach the program, a teacher's manual, and sets of student pages to accompany the equipment. This unit will be followed by other SCIS units until all of the units in the sequential K-6 program of SCIS are produced in this form. The production of materials in this way makes possible the trial of SCIS material in the centers and selected interested school systems. Since the SCIS philosophy states that the children themselves working directly with the materials are the basis for the science program, the printed materials are and will be available only in conjunction with the kit of equipment and materials.

The student pages referred to in relation to *Material Objects,* and the other printed materials under development for other units, differ significantly from the usual science textbooks for the elementary grades. Instructions for carrying out experiments, forms for recording information about experiments completed, and pages which pose problems and encourage discussion make up most of the pages in the student manuals. There are also pages to aid the teacher in areas of appraisal and evaluation, as described in this chapter.

Little reading material is included and the books therefore are valueless without the accompanying equipment. This is not to say that high quality reading materials on scientific subjects are not needed, but rather to indicate the desire to have them produced supplementary to but integrated with the development of the program and the pupils. Such a procedure would encourage interested pupils to go further on their own in areas of particular interest. The all-too-common reading about science from a textbook situation observed in so many classrooms today will not be possible when using SCIS materials.

This preliminary commercial publication program will make possible the trial of SCIS materials in the centers, since the necessary equipment, materials, and printed matter will now be available in quantities sufficient to supply the public schools directly associated with these centers. In addition, the production of these materials will make possible the trial by selected school systems over a period of years of all or part of the SCIS program. The concluding chapter in this book will explore the opportunities that this will create for the schools not only to gain information about the SCIS program but also to begin to develop their own administration and staff for the changes that are already underway in our approach to the subject of science in relation to elementary school children.

VIII

Getting Started

OVERVIEW

By taking a look in depth at the origins of, basis for, and development of the SCIS program, the first seven chapters of this book have raised many of the major points involved in the curriculum reform now taking place in elementary science. Within the next decade, many present conceptions and misconceptions of the nature of an elementary science program will be replaced. The ideas now being developed by a number of long-range, federally financed projects in science education will result in new written materials, in a re-thinking of the teacher's role, in a new conception of what a child does during the science period, and in a virtual conversion of the elementary school classroom into a laboratory where children can have direct science experiences.

Guiding the orderly evolution of the elementary science curriculum is the responsibility of all school people. There is no ready-made formula for doing this; no one can say now what is, or will be, the "right" program for any school district. The professional staff, therefore, must keep abreast of developments in the "new science" movement and decide for themselves what implications those developments have for re-thinking of their program.

There are presently four major elementary school projects operating with federal support in this country. As mentioned previously (in Chapter I), each has taken a somewhat different approach to re-designing the science program. The American Association for the Advancement of Science has adopted a process approach. Its materials call for children to examine in detail such processes of science as observing, classifying, recognizing number relations, communicating, measuring, and recognizing space/time relations. The Elementary Science Study of Educational Services, Inc., is working on individual units intended to give children experience in science. Topics such as "Growing Seeds," "Observing Mealworms," "Kitchen Physics," "Gases and Airs," and "Small Things" comprise the first units available from this study. The Minnemast Project of the University of Minnesota is working on an integrated approach to science and mathematics at the elementary school level. SCIS, which we have been describing in this book, is developing a sequential articulated program for the elementary school in order to increase scientific literacy. The program is based on the structure of science, and the presently developed units have been described in Chapter III.

Though significant differences exist in the approaches taken by each of these projects, it is important at the present time to emphasize their common features:

1. Enough equipment and materials are provided so that each individual can explore the aspect of science being studied.

2. The program is designed and materials are chosen only after careful consideration of the ways in which young children learn.

3. All of the projects involve university scientists in their direction.

4. The local school must spend a great deal of time, money, and effort to introduce successfully a science program based on their work.

Keeping in mind these common features and the differences as presented in Chapter I, it is important to look at the roles of the curriculum leader and the teacher in regard to the developing reform in the elementary school science curriculum. The next two sections of this chapter are addressed to these individuals. The last section suggests a group of activities which can be used in the schools at the present time. Experience with activities like these will help prepare the leader and school for the coming curriculum reform in science.

TO THE CURRICULUM LEADER

Probably the one individual in the school system most able to take responsibility for the orderly development of the new science is the curriculum leader. In some districts, this person is an elementary science specialist or consultant; in others he is a general curriculum consultant. In many districts the principal is the individual primarily responsible for curriculum leadership. Even where the services of a science specialist or general curriculum consultant are available, the role of the principal is of prime importance. He is the individual on the scene capable of interacting directly with the teachers and able to help them bring about the orderly adaption to change.

Few of the national projects are close to completing their work. The availability of a complete program, or of the opportunity to synthesize a complete program from the work of the many projects, is still some years in the future. But the curriculum leader should not delay action until such materials are available. To "sit it out" for the next several years would prevent growth and development that could take place immediately and therefore benefit the present crop of elementary school children, and deprive teachers of the kind of experience they will need to assimilate and use the new science programs when they are available. Instead, the alert, concerned administrator or curriculum leader should take the following steps to prepare his schools and teachers for change:

1. Encourage teachers and administrators to attend professional meetings where they can learn about the work of the science curriculum projects. (And make released time and travel funds available for this purpose.) Invite members of project staffs—or teachers who have helped test project materials—to serve as consultants in your district on inservice and teacher workshop days.

2. Obtain copies of printed materials already produced by the projects. (They are available at little or no cost from the projects themselves.) Place these in professional libraries so that interested teachers and administrators can study them. Form committees to review and analyze these printed materials—not to determine which is best but to promote understanding of current trends in elementary science curriculum development. In addition, these committees might select units or parts of units that seem suitable for experimental trial in your district. Committees like these should have secretarial services and either released time or other compensation (financial or salary credit) to help them accomplish this vital task.

3. Enroll interested teachers and administrators in summer conferences or college courses directly concerned with the new

curriculum developments in elementary science. In employing new staff members, give special consideration to qualified candidates who have such experience.

4. Experiment with the materials and equipment of the various projects using the findings of the committees described here and the experience of your staff members who have taken appropriate summer or college-year courses. The Science Curriculum Improvement Study, for example, is making its materials available through D. C. Heath and Company starting in the fall of 1966. Other projects have already or soon will be announcing publishing plans. Through experimentation with these new materials it is possible to inform teachers and pupils of the approaches of the curriculum reform movement in elementary science. Such information, when coupled with the other suggestions given in this list, will begin to bring about the necessary re-thinking of roles and re-examination of program necessary at this time.

5. Send emissaries to schools or university centers using these new programs so they can get a first-hand view of the new science. The purpose of the visit should not be to decide whether the programs are good or bad, but rather to observe how children work with the new science materials and to note how the new science affects the organization of the classroom and the school. Specific information about places where materials are being tested can be obtained from the individual projects.

By giving yourself and your teachers the opportunities described here, you, the curriculum leader, can guide elementary science as it evolves from a "read about it" science program to an "investigate it yourself" science program where the students and teachers can experience first-hand the interest, fun, and intellectual stimulation that comes from carrying out investigations. If you plan carefully, allowing time enough and providing for the necessary re-orienting and training of staff, you will avoid much of the anxiety and failure experienced by some districts when they tried to adopt the new math.

If your district already has moved significantly away from the "read about it" science program of the past, you should look at the foregoing as suggestions for re-examining your program to find where further improvement is possible. You might, for one thing, seek an opportunity to establish one of your schools as a test center for one or more of the elementary science curriculum projects.

Funds are available under the Elementary and Secondary Education Act of 1965 to carry out demonstration and training projects using the materials developed by one or more of the elementary school science studies. The National Science Foundation has a Cooperative College School Program which will support plans for the tryout of science innovations. This program has the advantage of requiring and supporting a working relationship with a neighboring college or university. Primarily, teacher-training activities are supported.

TO THE TEACHER

When the "new" mathematics arrived in the schools, it brought gray hairs to the head of many a primary grade teacher who was unprepared to teach it. Now the "new" science is coming. It, too, will produce a harvest of gray hairs, no doubt, but hopefully a scanty one compared to the last. The new science, for one reason, comes with more advance warning. It is still being developed and tested, and it will be a number of years before teaching materials are generally available. There is still time to prepare. You can begin your preparation now by experimenting with new ways of teaching the science you already know. The suggestions given here will guide you.

If you begin now, you will be ready when the change comes. Meanwhile, you will gain a delightful dividend in the immediate growth and improvement of your science teaching methods. And in addition, you will find that teaching the new science can be engrossing and enjoyable for you and your entire class.

Though the various national curriculum study groups differ in their approach to the new science, they recommend the use of the classroom as a laboratory where children can make discoveries about natural phenomena. In line with this idea, the teacher of the new science, then, is a "laboratory director" whose job is not to tell the children about science or listen to them while they read about science but to observe them while they are individually involved in science activities. He encourages the pupils to experiment to find answers to their questions. He uses the work of the children, their observations, and their questions as the basis of his planning for further science activities. In all of this, of course, he is guided by the

Using the classroom as a laboratory

content and structure of the school's science curriculum. This point of view was developed more fully in Chapter V.

As an example of this approach to science teaching, let us look at the problem of dissolving solid substances in water and then evaporating the solution to recover them. Such activities give children beginning experiences which will help them to develop an understanding of the conservation of substance. Let your pupils mix rock salt and water, then ask them such questions as "Where did the salt go?" and "Where is the salt now?" If the pupils describe the salt as disappearing, suggest mixing with it a colored substance such as Kool-Aid, Funny Face, or powdered paint. If, on the other hand, the children's comments and actions indicate some understanding of the dissolving process, you can proceed to ask, "What is your evidence?" and "How can we get the salt back?"

These questions will lead to further experiments. When you pose them to your pupils, accept all the suggestions they offer and let them test their ideas in actual experimentation. One or more of the children might suggest evaporating some of the liquid. If this is suggested, ask the children to do this and compare the remains with the original salt: "Is it the same?" "What is your evidence?" "Is it the salt we put into the water?" "How can we find out?"

Questions like these will lead to further questions and further experiments such as re-dissolving the evaporated salt and letting it evaporate once more.

Possibly no child will suggest evaporating the original mixture in order to regain the salt. In that case, after trying many of the children's suggestions, you can "invent" the idea of evaporating the mixture to see if anything will be left. In this instance, the work should proceed more slowly, and extensive experience in dissolving and evaporating many substances should precede any attempt to go further.

You, as teacher and "laboratory director," should, of course, match the pace of these activities to the abilities of your pupils. Your pupils will not achieve a complete understanding of the dissolving and evaporating processes. But they will acquire experience which, with further experience and maturation, will eventually lead to understanding.

Teaching science to young children in a laboratory setting can be an interesting challenge—provided you develop the necessary skills. College courses and district inservice programs may be of help in this respect. Independent study of modern high school science texts can do much to increase your knowledge of science concepts and facts.

When signing up for a college or inservice course, try to choose one that includes work in the laboratory. If you are studying a text that suggests an experiment that can be performed at home, carry it out. Laboratory experiences, formal or informal, will help you to understand and appreciate the processes of science, since they involve you in working with materials, making observations, and interpreting those observations. One cannot study the processes of science divorced from the content of science, but greater understanding of the content of science comes from personal experience with its processes.

These are things you can do as a professional person outside the classroom. Your work inside the classroom can also contribute to your developing ability as a science teacher. For a starter, look over the materials so far produced by the various curriculum projects. (Some of these may be available in your local curriculum library, or your principal may order them from the projects.)

From among these sources or from the activities given in the next section, choose one or two activities to test with your pupils—

either with the entire class or with a group of six or eight. Let the pupils do the work; listen carefully to their comments and their answers to your questions. Try to devise a second activity based on what takes place during the first. Continue to think of possibilities for laboratory-type experiences as you follow the adopted science program in your district or read the professional literature.

As you try a number of these kinds of activities, you may find two things happening: (1) You should discover more opportunities for laboratory-type teaching (they were there all along, but possibly you were not looking), and (2) it will become easier and more enjoyable for you and the children to conduct the science classroom in this fashion. The development of your skills is therefore a two-way process. On the one hand, you, as a professional person, are increasing your knowledge of the content and processes of science; at the same time, you are learning to work with pupils in a laboratory situation.

As discussed in Chapter V, the one thing that can make or break you in your role as a "laboratory director" is the technique you use in asking questions. Consider why you ask children questions. Is it to find out if they remember what you told them yesterday? Or to encourage thinking and discussion that will lead to further understanding? The kind and form of questions you ask makes the difference. For example, recall the questions phrased in the section of this chapter dealing with the dissolving of salt: "Where did the salt go?" "Where is the salt now?" "How do we get the salt back?" "What is your evidence?" Questions like these cause children to look more closely at the work they are doing, reconsider their observations, and try to develop an interpretation based on their own findings.

Contrast such questions with the "why" questions often heard in the primary grades. For example, "Why does the salt dissolve?" is completely unanswerable by young children unless you want them to say "Because you put it into water." "Why" questions are very complex for the young children and do little to increase a child's understanding of natural phenomena or his desire to explore a given situation further. When you formulate questions, therefore, always ask yourself, "Is my question a hunt for an answer? Or is it an attempt to encourage further questions and discussion that will eventually involve children in science and help develop their understanding?"

As you develop or help others develop science lessons judge the classroom activities by the following guidelines. These are not intended as a prescription for good elementary school science teaching; rather, they are points to keep in mind as lessons are planned:

1. The pupils are getting more actual experience working with materials in the science program. Time spent using the classroom as a laboratory is greater now than it was last week or last month.

2. Questions are asked in order to generate discussion, introduce new ideas, or set the stage for further activity on the part of the children. The emphasis is not on the answer, but rather on the observations and experiences that formed the basis for the answer. "Why" questions are avoided as much as possible.

3. Activities are selected for their potential contribution to the pupil's understanding of the basic structure of science. Summarizing, concluding, or completing a topic are not immediate goals of elementary science instruction.

Recording data in the student manual during an experiment

4. Listening to children, watching them at work, and planning further activities for them take up most of the science-teaching time. Talking about science and lecturing are reduced to a minimum.

Keep in mind that developing the science program and learning to teach it are continuing processes, then no one will need to be anxious or fearful when the new science materials become more generally available. In fact, the change will be looked upon as simply another step in the ongoing development of the science program in particular and the education program in general.

SUGGESTED ACTIVITIES

The following activities taken from the work of the Science Curriculum Improvement Study are suggested as good starting points for the teacher or school wanting to begin or further develop exploration of the kind of science program described in this book in general and this chapter in particular.

AN OBJECT HUNT

The suggestion, "Let's go on an object hunt," will be enthusiastically received by your kindergarten or first grade class. Precede it with a discussion of objects in the classroom. Boards, erasers, pencils, chalk, children, chairs, tables, goldfish, and so on, are interesting objects found in the classroom. During the discussion, encourage the children to describe some of the objects by their properties (rough, square, white) rather than by their uses. Our experience with primary children indicates that this discussion about objects and properties should be pupil-dominated. The teacher enters the discussion only to direct the descriptions toward properties or to mediate a controversy. When this is done, the subsequent sorting of objects by their properties will become meaningful and important to the children, and they will have little trouble grouping objects in this manner.

When you are ready for the object hunt, give each child a paper bag to hold the objects that he will collect during the hunt. The route should be chosen beforehand. Any convenient walk around the school grounds or through a nearby park is satisfactory. Suggest that each collect between five and ten objects. The only requirement is that all their objects must fit into their bag.

Now take the group over the chosen route and allow them to choose and collect items. The objects they pick up should be selected without your assistance. Use part of the trip to point out interesting objects and phenomena along the way. Restrict this discussion to objects which cannot or should not be collected such as birds, some flowers, trees, and large rocks. In the city, man-made objects such as buildings, benches, and street lights can be described.

After returning to the classroom, ask each child to place the objects he collected on his desk. By your questions, direct the description of the object to its properties. Questions such as "Is it hard?" or "Is it shiny?" help to focus the attention of the children on the properties of the object. After giving five or ten children (or more if they are interested) the opportunity to describe one of their objects, present the following problem: "Can you sort your objects into groups of different kinds?" If the previous discussion about objects and their properties was meaningful and extensive enough, the children will tend to sort the collected objects by some property common to part of the entire group in their bag. If not, you can either pick up the discussion about objects and their properties or can offer one or two suggestions such as using objects with corners in one group as a basis for sorting.

Once children have sorted their objects into groups, individual pupils can tell about the choices they made, or the class can play "detective" to figure out what property or properties the individual was thinking about when he sorted his objects. An example of an interesting type of question to ask now is, "If the objects in this group are all smooth (or shiny, or round, or hard—the property by which the child sorted), how would you describe the ones left over in the other groups?" The kind of answer the child gives to such a question will not only indicate his level of understanding about the sorting of objects, but will also indicate his ability to describe verbally what he has done. Does he see the relationship between the two categories—that one category is the opposite of the other—or does he simply say that the others don't belong in that category? For example, if he considers one group shiny, does he think of the rest as dull or simply not put them in the shiny category?

When the children have carried out a number of sortings of the objects they collected, suggest that everyone sort by the same property—for example, all rough objects in one group and all smooth objects in the other group. Some children may feel that certain objects are neither rough nor smooth and will wonder what to do with them. Discuss this problem but let them come to their own decision. There is no one right answer to a question like this. As long as the method the child adopts is used consistently by him, it is correct. Of course, during the discussion which follows, some children will call certain objects smooth that other children call rough. This disagreement is important, since it provides evidence for the concept that sorting alternatives such as smooth-rough, shiny-dull, hard-soft, or long-short are dependent not only on the individual objects but also on the collection of which they are a part. This is a difficult conceptual problem for young children, but observing and talking about situations such as this will help them develop an understanding of the idea.

If you try the object hunt and carry out the discussions and the sorting of objects collected, your children will have many experiences which will enable them to extend their knowledge of objects found in the natural (or man-made) environment around the school. The children will have experience in observing carefully and describing objects by their properties. The idea of grouping collections of objects by their properties will be introduced, and the children will develop some skill at this task. The concept that the decision about which group an object belongs in depends, to some extent, on the range of properties in the collection being sorted will be introduced. Some children will get at least a partial understanding of this idea.

The children can now gain further experience in grouping and sorting by working with collections of objects provided by you or brought from home. Samples of woods, metals, minerals, liquids, and gases can all be used for these grouping and sorting purposes. Activities of this type focus the attention of the children on the properties of the objects and help them develop their ability to observe material objects and communicate their observations to others. You can also use these activities to introduce the children to differences and similarities between different objects composed of the same material. A piece of pine wood and an envelope of pine sawdust are two interesting objects which can be used to illustrate this point.

These activities will give you the opportunity to observe your pupils using their initiative to construct their own approaches to a problem. Some of their ideas will surprise you. Enjoy the surprises. Use them to help evolve other activities which will provide further opportunities for your pupils to exercise their initiative. These experiences and the abilities developed through them will be used extensively in the science program throughout the elementary school and beyond. Careful observation of the phenomena of interest is a prerequisite to all further work in the sciences.

RECORDING VARIATION

Children who have had experience in describing, sorting, and grouping objects by their properties can be introduced to the scientific idea of variation. As with certain other units prepared by and available from the Science Curriculum Improvement Study, the objective of the unit, *Variation and Measurement*, is to give the children a start at looking at objects and at groups of objects in a more analytical way. In this description, an approach will be suggested by which you can introduce your class to the idea of variation. Once they have had experience with the technique, it is possible to apply the work on variation when predicting such things as the approximate height and weight of the next child to transfer into the class or the probable weather for April. The material presented in this description is suggested for the middle of the primary years. Older children who have not had the experience will also enjoy trying it.

How many peas are in a pod? This question or one like it will surely spark a discussion in your classroom. The children will soon realize that there is no one answer. They will probably have little information on which to base their responses. At this point, present the class with a population (a bag full) of fresh pea pods. Invite each child to come to a table to select a paper plate and three pea pods. Be sure to have many extra pods after all the children have three. (About two pounds of fresh peas provide enough pods for a class of thirty.) Once the children have their pods, discuss the properties of and the similarities and differences among the objects (the three pods) each child has received. (If fresh green peas are not available, two #303 cans of whole green beans will provide an alternate population for study.)

Develop a method with the children by which they can record the number of peas they find in each of their three pods. Each child should now open each of his pods, count the number of peas inside, and put the results on his record sheet. Don't oversell the idea of record keeping. It is, of course, most important in all work in science. The children, however, should learn its importance by experience; that is, by developing many experiments where the record from one part is important and useful in a later part.

Once the peas have been counted and the record completed, the pods and peas should be collected and discarded. Now ask, "Do you think all pea pods contain the same number of peas?" Differences in the number of peas found in each pod will become apparent. Ask how the children think one could find out more about the number of peas found in each pod. They will probably suggest asking each child about the number of peas in his pods. Try this and other ideas they might offer.

Comparing results will become cumbersome, and at this point you will "invent" the use of the histogram. Put a number line on the lower part of the chalkboard, extending from zero to about

FIGURE 9

Histogram of the number of peas found in each one of a sample of 41 pods

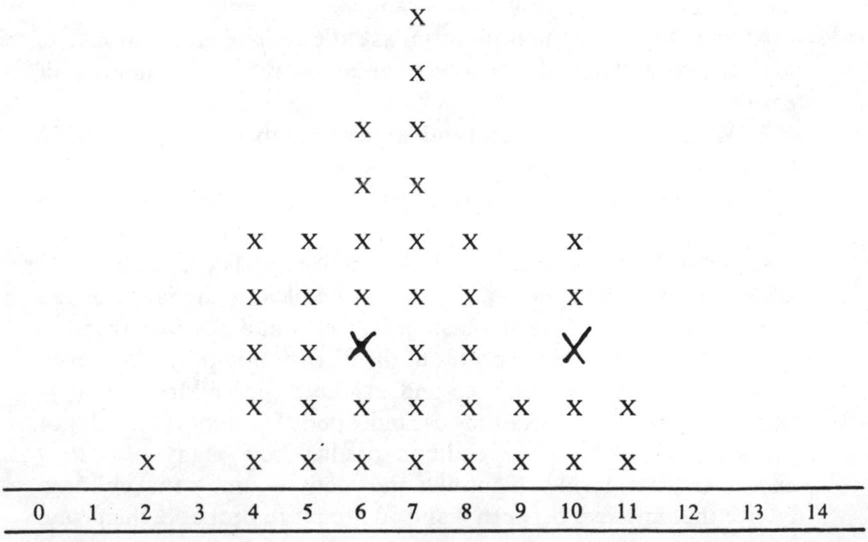

```
                          X
                          X
                    X     X
                    X     X
           X  X  X  X  X        X
           X  X  X  X  X        X
           X  X  X  X  X        X
           X  X  X  X  X  X  X  X
        X     X  X  X  X  X  X  X  X
     _____
     0  1  2  3  4  5  6  7  8  9  10  11  12  13  14
```

fifteen. An example of the number line and histogram is given in Figure 9. It shows a typical distribution for a sample of pea pods used in one class.

Ask each child to bring his record to the board and place an X above each numeral which represents the number of peas he found in one of his pods. Demonstrate this by putting the information for your three pods on the board first. (Of course, you too have a record; *everybody* does the experiment. When possible, it is a good idea to work along with the children during an experiment, since example is an excellent way of teaching experimental technique.) The children now do the same for each of the pods they have, placing one X above another wherever there is a duplication.

If you feel the group is ready for it, you can have the children make their own copy of the histogram at their seats. A sheet of paper with a mimeographed number line and dots to guide their X's is helpful to young children who have trouble placing them in a column. As each child comes forward to put his data on the board, you can again mention the importance of keeping a record, since it now allows the child to share his information with the whole class.

The numbers used in the rest of this discussion are taken from the results presented in the histogram shown in Figure 9 on page 155. Although the results are typical, the ones you find in your class may vary considerably from these. This is not important since the results are given only as an example.

After completing the histogram, ask the following questions:

1. Do you think all the pods contained the same number of peas?

2. What was the smallest (and largest) number of peas found in any one pod?

3. What was the one number of peas found most often in a single pod?

4. About how many peas did most of our pods contain?

Questions such as these will develop the idea of the range of the distribution (2 to 11 in the histogram here) and the fact that the results cluster around the center of the distribution (4 to 10 or even 6 to 9). The way to reinforce and evaluate the children's understanding of these ideas is to choose more pods from the remainder of the sample and have the children predict how many peas they expect to find inside. Continue this activity until the children realize that answers between 4 and 10 are more probable than, say,

2 or 12. The children should realize that 2 or 12 are possible but somewhat less probable than the other answers.

Other samples such as beans in whole green bean pods, leaflets on ash leaves, and perhaps even raisins in a slice of raisin bread can be used to study variation and allow the children to make discoveries about the use of the histogram. The different kinds of samples may produce different-looking distributions; therefore, the fact that the kind of prediction you can make depends upon the nature of the distribution becomes apparent.

After you have introduced your class to the measurement of height and weight, plotting histograms for the variation of these quantities within your class provides an interesting experience for the children. They can now predict the approximate size of the next child to transfer into the class. Considering the present mobility of our population, you will probably have many opportunities to try making these height and weight predictions.

EVIDENCE OF INTERACTION

Children who have had extensive experience observing, describing, and grouping objects are now ready to consider the question of what happens between two objects. You will define this happening as *evidence of interaction*, and the children will develop the ability to find many examples of evidence of interaction. In order to focus the child's attention on the objects of interest at the time, you will also introduce the concept of *systems of objects*.

Children, who tend to look at events in a comprehensive, subjective, and non-analytical way, must learn to recognize regular patterns of behavior. During the course of these activities, the children will, first of all, apply their knowledge of material objects by identifying the objects that are present and seem to be connected with the happening. The second step will be for the children to recognize that changes are taking place during the period of observation. These may, for example, be changes in shape, position, color, temperature, or appearance. The third step is to decide which object or objects were instrumental in causing the change. This step is the one that leads to the interaction concept.

An observation of change is evidence of interaction. The statement that objects interact transmits little information, whereas a description of the evidence of interaction clarifies what has happened between the objects of interest. For example, the statement that a magnet and a nail interacted has little meaning, since it could be an aluminum nail and the actual evidence of interaction be the fact that the magnet is hanging on the wall supported by the nail. This evidence is quite different from the case in which the magnet attracts and holds suspended an iron nail. Yet in both cases, we can say that the magnet and the nail interacted.

The first step is made necessary by the fact that in some way all objects in our complex universe are continually interacting with each other. The situation is just too complicated for child or scientist. The children therefore learn by experience (as the scientist does) to confine their attention to a few objects that are at the moment interesting because they participate in the striking changes that are taking place. We define this group of objects as our *system* for the experiment. Of course, objects in the system do interact with objects outside, but the effects of these interactions are less striking or less interesting for the observer at the time he chooses his system for an experiment.

Your use of this background information to tell the children about evidence of interaction and systems will do little to increase their understanding of the concepts involved. It *is* necessary, of course, for you to "invent" these terms for the children, but this "invention" must be preceded and followed by extensive opportunities for the children to have experience observing systems of interacting objects. Only through such experience and discussion, not only with you but among themselves, will the children have the opportunity to "discover" the conceptual meaning of the terms *evidence of interaction* and *system*. You should provide many opportunities for the children to observe phenomena in which they can describe the evidence of interaction between certain objects and also specify the system of interest for the experiment. Listed here are some activities which have been found useful in providing the children with experience in specifying systems of objects and in finding evidence of interaction.

Activity 1: A cardboard box of objects is passed out to the children, working in groups of two or four. It contains such objects as a card, a crayon, a magnet; a paper clip, a dry cell, a piece of wire with a flashlight bulb attached, a piece of clay, a stick, a pair of scissors, a cylinder with a hole in it, a piece of string, a thumbtack, a jar of water, a little tempera paint, and any other objects you care to include.

Children are invited to choose two objects and have them do something to each other. After they have had time to make choices and experiment on their own, individuals are asked to report on their experiment. In each of the reports, direct their attention to the evidence of interaction which is observed. For example, the magnet holds up the paper clip, or the crayon and card interacted and now there is writing on the card. (Do your children also report that the crayon is smaller to a very minute degree?)

The point at which you introduce the terminology, *evidence of interaction*, is a matter of personal choice and should be based on your understanding of the group with which you are working. You should probably introduce this terminology during the work with the objects from the boxes. Of course, this choosing, experimentation, and description can be carried out more than once. Use the same objects or vary them somewhat.

Observing evidence of interaction

Activity 2: Vinegar, bromthymol blue indicator (available in most swimming-pool supply stores), a few empty jars, a balloon pump, and a few balloons are interesting objects to choose for providing further experience. A little bromthymol blue (enough to turn the water blue) is added to the water in each of two jars. Can your children think of the liquid inside as one object and the jar itself as a second object? What object did the liquid displace?

Now pour some water into one jar containing bromthymol blue and water, and some vinegar into the other. Do the children observe evidence of interaction between the blue liquid and the water? The bubbles and movement of the water on mixing are evidence of interaction, but not very striking evidence. What about the interaction between the blue liquid and the vinegar? (The yellow color of the previously blue liquid is, of course, dramatic evidence of interaction in this case.) Ask your children to choose a system for this experiment. Can they think of the blue liquid and the vinegar as the objects taking part in the experiment and therefore define them as the system? Don't worry if they cannot. The ability to choose systems effectively when describing experiments develops after extensive experience—not the first or even the second time you mention it.

Now mix some bromthymol blue and water in each of two more jars. Have the children blow up one balloon with the balloon pump and one with their mouths. Allow the gas inside the balloons to bubble out through the blue liquid. Do the children notice any evidence of interaction in each case? What system do they choose for explaining each experiment? You may want to demonstrate these experiments the first time, but then give the children ample opportunity to experiment on their own with these interesting and not so common systems of objects.

Activity 3: Photographic proof paper exposed to the sun or a bright light shows evidence of interaction. What system do your children choose for this experiment? Do they think of sunlight as an object? Don't worry about the answer. A good case can be made for both the positive and negative reply. The important thing for early elementary school children is not so much to answer such questions as to confront them. When you or someone else is ready to develop a theory of light with these children, this experience will be invaluable in helping them to understand the theory.

What about the idea of considering a shadow on the wall as

evidence of interaction between a light source and an object (possibly you) between the light and the wall? Present this idea to your pupils and allow them to choose a system for the experiment.

Any and all situations in which objects interact can be used as the basis for further experiments through which children get experience in thinking of evidence of interaction and are asked to specify the system for their experiment. The playground, with such examples as the interaction between child and swing or child and child on the teeter-totter, is a good illustration of a place where this experience can be structured by a few well-placed teacher comments and questions. Many other possibilities will become immediately apparent to you. Use as many as are interesting to your group and feasible when considering the time available. In all cases, encourage the children to select and specify the system of objects they are interested in and have them describe the evidence of interaction they observe.

Since you are trying to develop in the children a way of looking at natural phenomena which they will use throughout their study of science, be patient, and realize that it takes time for this ability to become a part of the child. You may find it valuable to do some of these experiments at one time and then pick up the story a week or two later. Since the introduction of this material is intended primarily for older primary school children, you should not expect to develop fully the concepts involved. You are introducing a point of view which will dominate the child's further experience with science. (Give him time to assimilate these ideas and reconstruct in his own mind his understanding of the concepts of choosing a system and describing happenings as evidence of interaction.)

SOLUTIONS

Pupils have observed the dissolving of a solid in a liquid many times. They have made a beverage by adding powder to water, or have sweetened tea or lemonade by adding sugar. Although all of this commonsense experience is important, not all of it is particularly useful in the study of science. In this group of activities, you will give your children the opportunity to take a look at solutions from an entirely different point of view.

In the first activity, their attention will be focussed on the fact that a solution is a system made up of two or more objects. In addition, they will learn from experience that these objects in the system can be separated from each other. The experience of recovering the dissolved material from the solution (separating the objects in the system) will help to build and reinforce the concept of the conservation of matter. That is, the material they dissolve in the liquid is not destroyed but can actually be recovered from the liquid where its presence may not be visible. In the second activity, the children will be introduced to the meaning of *concentration* of a solution.

Another important aspect of these activities on solutions is the opportunity they provide for emphasizing once again the value of keeping records. The children will be making observations on their individual systems and later you and they will want to discuss their findings. Either have the children keep records in their own way or prepare duplicated outline sheets on which they will fill in their records. Which choice you make depends to a large extent on the group you are working with and your style of teaching. Obviously, if you provide an outline, the records will be quite similar, and therefore easier to compare. However, if the children develop their own, some will provide interesting information which your form does not ask them to give. The records, however, will be much more incomplete and it will be harder to compare them. Try both approaches, evaluate the results, and evolve an approach to this question of record keeping for yourself. Your approach, of course, will have to be modified for each new group of learners.

Activity 1: Dissolving and Evaporation. In the first part of this activity, your pupils will have the opportunity to discover some ideas about solutions. They will mix various solid substances with water in order to form solutions. Any or all of the following substances can be used: cobalt chloride, copper chloride, copper nitrate, and copper sulfate, all of which produce colored solutions when dissolved in water; sodium chloride (table salt), nickel sulfate, potassium chloride, potassium nitrate, and sodium thiosulfate (photographic hypo), all of which form colorless solutions with water. (If you do not have a supply of any of these substances, you can obtain them from a science supply house or possibly from the high school science department in your district.)

Give each child one or more small envelopes, each filled with one of the substances listed above. Also give each child one or more small jars or vials of water. A few paper towels and an old cafeteria tray for each child will help to keep the ingredients under control.

Ask the children to mix one solid substance with the water in one of the jars. Let them do this in any way they want the first time. Encourage the children to observe carefully while making their solution. Discuss with the group the solutions they have produced in their experiment. Are the children able to describe what has happened to the solid material they placed in the jar? Where do they think the solid material is after it has dissolved in the water? Ask what would happen if they poured a little of their solution into a shallow dish and let it dry out.

Each child should let some of his solution evaporate to dryness. In its work with the children, SCIS has them use a medicine dropper to remove a little solution and squirt it onto a watch glass in order to let it dry. If you do not have medicine droppers or watch glasses for each child, they can simply pour a little solution out onto any glass or plastic dish or container or even onto a piece of aluminum foil with the sides bent up to form a crude cup. After the water has evaporated (a day or two), have the children observe the residue and see if they can relate the residue to the substance they originally dissolved in the water. If the children have kept records they will know the name of the substance they used to make their solution. À display set of all the substances used will provide the children with a way of comparing the appearance of the residue with the appearance of the material they dissolved in the water.

Observing the dissolving process: getting ready to do an evaporation experiment

Provide opportunities for the children to do similar dissolving and evaporation experiments with other substances and materials. Each child should have the opportunity to use materials which produce both colored and colorless solutions. As a contrasting activity, give the children some copper oxide, small rocks, grass seeds, or other materials that they cannot dissolve in water. Experiences like these will help the children to discover the differences between a true solution and a mixture.

Activity 2: Concentration of Solutions. *Concentration* here is used to refer to the actual amount of dissolved material in a certain amount of solution. For example, a salt solution may contain one ounce of salt in one gallon of solvent. A solution made by dissolving four ounces of salt in a gallon of solvent has a different concentration. When using a colored dissolved material like copper chloride, differences in concentration can be observed visually, since the more concentrated solution will be a deeper color than the less concentrated solution. The concentration of a solution can be varied by varying either the amount of material dissolved or the amount of liquid used to dissolve it. In this activity, your pupils will add different amounts of solid material to the same amount of liquid in order to gain experience in making solutions of differing concentrations. Of course, as an additional activity, you can set up the situation where the children use the same amount of solid material and different amounts of water.

Arrange the children in groups of four or five. Give each group a number of small envelopes each filled with the same amount of copper chloride or one of the other salts which produced a colored solution in Activity 1. Each child in the group should have a jar or cup filled with water. All the jars should be the same size and contain the same amount of water. Before class, make a solution using two envelopes of solid material and a jar with an amount of water equal to the one you gave the children. Show the children your solution and tell them that you want each group to make at least one solution which will be darker and one which will be lighter. If you use jars with caps, the children can mix their solutions by shaking them. Otherwise, popsicle sticks or some other stirrers will be needed.

When the groups have finished, have them come up to the front of the room so they can compare the color of their solution to the color of yours. Tell the children you used two envelopes of solid material to make your solution. Ask them how many they used to make the lighter and darker solutions displayed. Arrange three jars in order from dark to light. Review the number of envelopes of solid material used to make each solution. Ask the children how much water was used in each case. Relate the darkness of the solution to the number of envelopes of solid material used to make the solution. Introduce the use of the term "most concentrated" for the one containing the most solid material. Use the term "least concentrated" to describe the solution lightest in color.

With a clean medicine dropper, take three drops of solution from each jar. Place the liquid from each jar on a different watch glass or other evaporating surface. Label each glass and allow the water to evaporate from all three. Let the children observe the solid material remaining in each watch glass and ask them to decide whether this test tells which of the three jars contained the most solid material.

On another day, determine whether your class understands concentration by giving each group four empty jars, a pitcher of water, and four envelopes of solid material. Tell the children that they must use one envelope of solid material in each jar but that they should produce solutions of differing concentrations. Observe carefully what the different groups do to solve this problem. From an evaluation of your observations, you can structure additional activities on concentration for your class.

TEMPERATURE

Place three jars on your desk or demonstration table. Fill the first one with water and ice cubes, the second with water at room temperature and the third with hot water. Ask one child to put one finger in the jar with ice water and one in the jar of water at room temperature. Have another pupil put one finger in the room-temperature water and one in the hot water. Ask the pupils if they think the water in the middle jar is hot or cold. Repeat this activity with more children. The controversy and confusion which ensue will illustrate the subjective nature of the response of the human body's sensory elements.

Our skin contains sensory elements which react to a change in temperature. We instinctively interpret this change as evidence that an object is hot or cold. Of course, this interpretation may be confusing as illustrated by the three jars of water. In this group of activities, you will give the children the opportunity to observe other temperature indicators. Any device that easily shows evidence of interaction with hot or cold objects can be used as a temperature indicator. A drop of water, for example, is frequently used to test the temperature of an electric iron; if it sizzles, the iron is hot. A pat of butter may be used to estimate the temperature of a piece of toast; if it melts, the toast is warm enough. Such indicators operate effectively only over a narrow range of temperature and they do not lend themselves to making a scale on which temperature differences can be determined. The standard liquid-in-glass thermometer is therefore used when more nearly accurate information is needed. In these activities you will introduce the children to the skill of reading the thermometer. Then they will use the thermometer to study systems made up of objects at different temperatures. In the last activity, you will introduce thermal equilibrium.

Activity 1: Invention of Temperature. In this activity you will first introduce your class to the use of thermometers. It is possible to teach your children the use of the thermometers by rote in a much shorter time than this activity will take. It is known however, from experience, that approaching it as described here will allow the children to gain experience needed to really understand it. In giving instructions on the thermometer, there are four points to remember:

1. Think of the red liquid inside the thermometer as a system that can interact with other objects or systems.

2. The state or appearance of the liquid is described with the help of a number line printed along the glass tube.

3. Most of the liquid is in the little bulb at the end of the tube. To bring about a change in the liquid, something must interact with the liquid in the bulb.

4. The length of the liquid column is a property of the liquid. By experimentation, it has been found that the length depends on warmness or coldness. A measure of length can be used as a measure of temperature.

These four points are for your information. The children should come to know and understand them through actual experience using thermometers. A large demonstration model of the thermometer can be used to point out the various parts of the thermometer. Moving the red line along the scale of such a model provides experience in how to read the scale of a real thermometer. Let the children take readings of the position of the red line.

Give each child a small thermometer of the type usually used as an inexpensive room thermometer. Ask the children to read the number line to determine the temperature of the red liquid. Have jars of alcohol in various places around the room. Let each child dip his thermometer bulb into the alcohol and then remove it. He will observe changes in the temperature of the red liquid when he removes the thermometer from the alcohol. Have him read the number line in order to describe the temperature of the red liquid. Challenge pupils to change the temperature of the red liquid in other ways. Who can record the highest and lowest temperature of it?

So far you have emphasized the red liquid and spoken only of its temperature. However, if thermometers measured only the temperature of the liquid inside, they would be rather valueless devices. What must be illustrated, therefore, is that the temperature of the red liquid that the thermometer measures is also the temperature of the system or object in contact with the bulb, provided that the two have come to equilibrium.

Conclude Activity 1 by placing many jars of water at differing temperatures around the room. Let pupils in groups of three or four use their thermometers to find the temperature of the water in their jar. The fact that after a while all thermometers in the same jar will read about the same will reinforce the idea that thermometers measure water temperature.

Give the children other experiences determining the temperature of objects and systems with the thermometer. Some of these systems such as well stirred water may show a single temperature. For contrast, devise some systems that are not at a single temperature. Pour hot sand in one side of a tray and cold sand in the other side. Ask the children to find the temperature of the sand. As another example, sink an ice cube in water by tying it to a coin. Ask the children to find the temperature of the water without stirring it up. Experiences such as these will help the children to realize that a system may not be all at a single temperature. Rather, we may want to discuss parts of a system, or subsystems.

The value of this part of the activity depends on your willingness to let children explore these systems and discuss their findings. Your role is that of an observer, available for help, but mainly interested in listening and watching.

Activity 2: Your introduction of thermal equilibrium to the children is a significant conceptual step forward. The children will need a great deal of experience, however, before they develop a real understanding of this.

Give each child a thermometer and place a jar or beaker of hot water in front of each group of two or four children. Ask them to place their thermometers in the jar of water and have them observe and record the temperatures of the thermometers. The children should continue to observe the thermometers as the water in the jar is allowed to interact with the air in the room. What happens to the temperature of the water in the jar? How much lower will the temperature go? Questions like these will tell you whether the children have any valid preconceptions about thermal equilibrium. Do they expect the temperature to keep dropping or do they relate its eventual level to the room temperature? These systems of jar, water, and thermometers can be observed occasionally all day.

After one or more experiments of this type, give each child a thermometer again. Have them team up in groups of two. Give each group two different-sized jars. Put hot water in the small jar and cold in the large one. The amount of water and jars used should be chosen so that the little one can be placed in the big one without spilling any water. Children should take the temperature of each jar of water at the beginning of the experiment. Demonstrate putting the smaller one into the larger one and ask the children to predict the changes they expect to take place in the two readings.

Have them do the experiment, read the thermometers, and record the results every minute for 5 or 10 minutes. Now ask them to predict the final temperature of the thermometers in each jar. Do they have a concept of thermal equilibrium or do they think the hot one will cool indefinitely and the cold one rise indefinitely? Either way, give your group more experiences with variations of this experiment.

Through experiences of this kind you can introduce your group to the concept of thermal equilibrium. Do not expect complete understanding, since you are only introducing a broad concept. But the experiences will be interesting and satisfying and will provide practice with the thermometer.

CONCLUSION

Whenever possible, the level of involvement of the child in these activities and in the science program as a whole must be individual and direct, with the child manipulating and observing the objects or systems under study. Extensive opportunities should be provided for the children to discuss among themselves what they have observed. The activities suggested meet these requirements and will help achieve the desired changes in pupil behavior.

After you have tried some of these activities, you will have noticed interesting changes in the way your pupils approach problems, and you will be partially convinced of the validity of the approach described in these sections. But these do not make up a science program. What can you do from day to day, all year long, to continue to build this approach into your science teaching?

Two suggestions are offered. First, by reading professional magazines, attending professional meetings, and in general seeking out information, keep abreast of the developments taking place in the curriculum reform movement now underway in elementary school science.

Second, reread the suggestions regarding the role of the teacher in the classroom and incorporate them into your procedures. Act as the teacher-observer and whenever possible put the equipment and materials in the hands of the children. These two tasks, neither easy to accomplish, will go a long way toward helping you develop a science program which is more meaningful for the children in your class. It will help you to "train" yourself so that when the results of the work of the various curriculum projects do become available widely, you will be able to make wise decisions about their applicability to and usefulness in your teaching situation. You will also become better able to make full use of whatever approach you and your school system finally adopt. You will get started.

Appendix

Cognitive Development in Children:
Development and Learning*

Jean Piaget

Center for Genetic Epistemology,
Geneva, Switzerland

My dear colleagues, I am very concerned about what to say to you, because I do not know if I shall accomplish the end that has been assigned to me. But I have been told that the important thing is not what you say, but the discussion which follows and the answers to questions you are asked. So this morning I shall simply give a general introduction of a few ideas which seem to me to be important for the subject of this conference.

First I would like to make clear the difference between two problems: the problem of *development* in general and the problem of *learning*. I think these problems are very different, although some people do not make this distinction.

The development of knowledge is a spontaneous process, tied to the whole process of embryogenesis. Embryogenesis concerns the development of the body, but it concerns as well the development of the nervous system and the development of mental functions. In the case of the development of knowledge in children, embryogenesis ends only in adulthood. It is a total development process which we must re-situate in its general biological and psychological context. In other words, development is a process which concerns the totality of the structures of knowledge.

Learning presents the opposite case. In general, learning is provoked by situations—provoked by a psychological experimenter;

*Reprinted through the permission of the *Journal of Research in Science Teaching* (1964), Vol. 2, pp. 176–186.

or by a teacher, with respect to some didactic point; or by an external situation. It is provoked, in general, as opposed to spontaneous. In addition, it is a limited process—limited to a single problem, or to a single structure.

So I think that development explains learning, and this opinion is contrary to the widely held opinion that development is a sum of discrete learning experiences. For some psychologists development is reduced to a series of specific learned items, and development is thus the sum, the cumulation of this series of specific items. I think this is an atomistic view which deforms the real state of things. In reality, development is the essential process and each element of learning occurs as a function of total development, rather than being an element which explains development. I shall begin, then, with a first part dealing with development, and I shall talk about learning in the second part.

To understand the development of knowledge, we must start with an idea which seems central to me—the idea of an *operation*. Knowledge is not a copy of reality. To know an object, to know an event, is not simply to look at it and make a mental copy or image of it. To know an object is to act on it. To know is to modify, to transform the object, and to understand the process of this transformation, and as a consequence to understand the way the object is constructed. An operation is thus the essence of knowledge; it is an interiorized action which modifies the object of knowledge. For instance an operation would consist of joining objects in a class to construct a classification. Or an operation would consist of ordering, or putting things in a series. Or an operation would consist of counting, or of measuring. In other words, it is a set of actions modifying the object, and enabling the knower to get at the structures of the transformation.

An operation is an interiorized action. But, in addition, it is a reversible action; that is, it can take place in both directions, for instance, adding or subtracting, joining or separating. So it is a particular type of action which makes up logical structures.

Above all, an operation is never isolated. It is always linked to other operations, and as a result it is always a part of a total structure. For instance, a logical class does not exist in isolation; what exists is the total structure of classification. An asymmetrical relation does not exist in isolation. Seriation is the natural, basic operational structure. A number does not exist in isolation. What exists is the series of numbers which constitute a structure, an exceedingly rich structure whose various properties have been revealed by mathematicians.

These operational structures are what seem to me to constitute the basis of knowledge, the natural psychological reality, in terms of which we must understand the development of knowledge. And the central problem of development is to understand the formation, elaboration, organization, and functioning of these structures.

I should like to review the stages of development of these structures, not in any detail, but simply as a reminder. I shall distinguish four main stages. The first is a sensory-motor, pre-verbal stage, lasting approximately the first 18 months of life. During this stage is developed the practical knowledge which constitutes the substructure of later representational knowledge. An example is the construction of the schema of the permanent object. For an infant, during the first months, an object has no permanence. When it disappears from the perceptual field it no longer exists. No attempt is made to find it again. Later, the infant will try to find it, and he will find it by localizing it spatially. Consequently, along with the construction of the permanent object there comes the construction of practical or sensory-motor space. There is similarly the construction of temporal succession, and of elementary sensory-motor causality. In other words, there is a series of structures which are indispensable for the structures of later representational thought.

In a second stage, we have pre-operational representation—the beginnings of language, of the symbolic function, and therefore of thought, or representation. But at the level of representational thought, there must now be a reconstruction of all that was developed on the sensory-motor level. That is, the sensory-motor actions are not immediately translated into operations. In fact, during all this second period of pre-operational representations, there are as yet no operations as I defined this term a moment ago. Specifically, there is as yet no conservation which is the psychological criterion of the presence of reversible operations. For example, if we pour liquid from one glass to another of a different shape, the pre-operational child will think there is more in one than in the other. In the absence of operational reversibility, there is no conservation of quantity.

In a third stage the first operations appear, but I call these concrete operations because they operate on objects, and not yet on verbally expressed hypotheses. For example, there are the operations of classification, ordering, the construction of the idea of number, spatial and temporal operations, and all the fundamental operations of elementary logic of classes and relations, of elementary mathematics, of elementary geometry, and even of elementary physics.

Finally, in the fourth stage, these operations are surpassed as the child reaches the level of what I call formal or hypothetic-deductive operations; that is, he can now reason on hypotheses, and not only on objects. He constructs new operations, operations of propositional logic, and not simply the operations of classes, relations, and numbers. He attains new structures which are on the one hand combinatorial, corresponding to what mathematicians call lattices; on the other hand, more complicated group structures. At the level of concrete operations, the operations apply within an immediate neighborhood: for instance, classification by successive inclusions. At the level of the combinatorial, however, the groups are much more mobile.

These, then, are the four stages which we identify, whose formation we shall now attempt to explain.

What factors can be called upon to explain the development from one set of structures to another? It seems to me that there are four main factors: first of all, *maturation*, in the sense of Gesell, since this development is a continuation of the embryogenesis; second, the role of *experience* of the effects of the physical environment on the structures of intelligence; third, *social transmission* in the broad sense (linguistic transmission, education, etc.); and fourth, a factor which is too often neglected but one which seems to me fundamental and even the principal factor. I shall call this the factor of *equilibration* or if you prefer it, of self-regulation.

Let us start with the first factor, maturation. One might think that these stages are simply a reflection of an interior maturation of the nervous system, following the hypotheses of Gesell, for example. Well, maturation certainly does play an indispensable role and must not be ignored. It certainly takes part in every transformation that takes place during a child's development. However, this first factor is insufficient in itself. First of all, we know practically nothing about the maturation of the nervous system beyond the first months of the child's existence. We know a little bit about it during the first two years but we know very little following this time. But above all, maturation doesn't explain everything, because the average ages at which these stages appear (the average chronological ages) vary a great deal from one society to another. The ordering of these stages is constant and has been found in all the societies studied. It has been found in various countries where psychologists in universities have redone the experiments but it has also been found in African peoples for example, in the children of the Bushmen, and in Iran, both in the villages and in the cities. However, although the order of succession is constant, the chronological ages of these stages vary a great deal. For instance, the ages which we have found in Geneva are not necessarily the ages which you would find in the United States. In Iran, furthermore, in the city of Teheran, they found approximately the same ages as we found in Geneva, but there is a systematic delay of two years in the children in the country. Canadian psychologists who redid our experiments, Monique Laurendeau and Father Adrien Pinard, found once again about the same ages in Montreal. But when they redid the experiments in Martinique, they found a delay of four years in all the experiments and this in spite of the fact that the children in Martinique go to a school set up according to the French system and the French curriculum and attain at the end of this elementary school a certificate of higher primary education. There is then a delay of four years, that is, there are the same stages, but systematically delayed. So you see that these age variations show that maturation does not explain everything.

I shall go on now to the role played by experience. Experience of objects, of physical reality, is obviously a basic factor in the development of cognitive structures. But once again this factor does not explain everything. I can give two reasons for this. The first reason is that some of the concepts which appear at the beginning of the stage of concrete operations are such that I cannot see how they could be drawn from experience. As an example, let us take the conservation of the substance in the case of changing the shape of a ball of plasticene. We give this ball of plasticene to a child who changes its shape into a sausage form and we ask him if there is the same amount of matter, that is, the same amount of substance as there was before. We also ask him if it now has the same weight and thirdly if it now has the same volume. The volume is measured by the displacement of water when we put the ball or the sausage into a glass of water. The findings, which have been the same every time this experiment has been done, show us that first of all there is conservation of the amount of substance. At about eight years old a child will say, "There is the same amount of plasticene." Only later does the child assert that the weight is conserved and still later that the volume is conserved. So I would ask you where the idea of the conservation of substance can come from. What is a constant and invariant substance when it doesn't yet have a constant weight or a constant volume? Through perception you can get at the weight of the ball or the volume of the ball but perception cannot give you an idea of the amount of substance. No experiment, no experience can show the child that there is the same amount of substance. He can weigh the ball and that would lead to the conservation of weight. He can immerse it in water and that would lead to the conservation of volume. But the notion of substance is attained before either weight or volume. This conservation of substance is simply a logical necessity. The child now understands that when there is a transformation something must be conserved because by reversing the transformation you can come back to the point of departure and once again have the ball. He knows that something is conserved but he doesn't know what. It is not yet the weight, it is not yet the volume; it is simply a logical form—a logical necessity. There, it seems to me, is an example of a progress in knowledge, a logical necessity for something to be conserved even though no experience can have led to this notion.

My second objection to the sufficiency of experience as an explanatory factor is that this notion of experience is a very equivocal one. There are, in fact, two kinds of experience which are psychologically very different and this difference is very important from the pedagogical point of view. It is because of the pedagogical importance that I emphasize this distinction. First of all, there is what I shall call physical experience, and, secondly, what I shall call logical-mathematical experience.

Physical experience consists of acting upon objects and drawing some knowledge about the objects by abstraction from the objects. For example, to discover that this pipe is heavier than this watch, the child will weigh them both and find the difference in the objects themselves. This is experience in the usual sense of the term—in the sense used by empiricists. But there is a second type of experience which I shall call logical mathematical experience where the knowledge is not drawn from the objects, but it is drawn by the actions effected upon the objects. This is not the same thing. When one acts upon objects, the objects are indeed there, but there is also the set of actions which modify the objects.

I shall give you an example of this type of experience. It is a nice example because we have verified it many times in small children under seven years of age, but it is also an example which one of my mathematician friends has related to me about his own childhood, and he dates his mathematical career from this experience. When he was four or five years old—I don't know exactly how old, but a small child—he was seated on the ground in his garden and he was counting pebbles. Now to count these pebbles he put them in a row and he counted them one, two, three, up to ten. Then he finished counting them and started to count them in the other direction. He began by the end and once again he found ten. He found this marvelous that there were ten in one direction and ten in the other direction. So he put them in a circle and counted them that way and found ten once again. Then he counted them in the other direction and found ten once more. So he put them in some other arrangement and kept counting them and kept finding ten. There was the discovery that he made.

Now what indeed did he discover? He did not discover a property of pebbles; he discovered a property of the action of ordering. The pebbles had no order. It was his action which introduced a linear order or a cyclical order, or any kind of an order. He discovered that the sum was independent of the order. The order was the action which he introduced among the pebbles. For the sum the same principle applied. The pebbles had no sum; they were simply in a pile. To make a sum, action was necessary—the operation of putting together and counting. He found that the sum was independent of the order, in other words, that the action of putting together is independent of the action of ordering. He discovered a property of actions and not a property of pebbles. You may say that it is in the nature of pebbles to let this be done to them and this is true. But it could have been drops of water, and drops of water would not have let this be done to them because two drops of water and two drops of water do not make four drops of water as you know very well. Drops of water then would not let this be done to them, we agree to that.

So it is not the physical property of pebbles which the experience uncovered. It is the properties of the actions carried out on the pebbles, and this is quite another form of experience. It is the point of departure of mathematical deduction. The subsequent deduction will consist of interiorizing these actions and then of combining them without needing any pebbles. The mathematician no longer needs his pebbles. He can combine his operations simply with symbols, and the point of departure of this mathematical deduction is logical–mathematical experience, and this is not at all experience in the sense of the empiricists. It is the beginning of the coordination of actions, but this coordination of actions before the stage of operations needs to be supported by concrete material. Later, this coordination of actions leads to the logical–mathematical structures. I believe that logic is not a derivative of language. The source of logic is much more profound. It is the total co-ordination of actions, actions of joining things together, or ordering things, etc. This is what logical–mathematical experience is. It is an experience of the actions of the subject, and not an experience of objects themselves. It is an experience which is necessary before there can be operations. Once the operations have been attained this experience is no longer needed and the coordinations of actions can take place by themselves in the form of deduction and construction for abstract structures.

The third factor is social transmission–linguistic transmission or educational transmission. This factor, once again, is funda-mental. I do not deny the role of any one of these factors; they all play a part. But this factor is insufficient because the child can receive valuable information via language or via education directed by an adult only if he is in a state where he can understand this information. That is, to receive the information he must have a structure which enables him to assimilate this information. This is why you cannot teach higher mathematics to a five-year-old. He does not yet have structures which enable him to understand.

I shall take a much simpler example, an example of linguistic transmission. As my very first work in the realm of child psychology, I spent a long time studying the relation between a part and a whole in concrete experience and in language. For example, I used Burt's test employing the sentence, "Some of my flowers are buttercups." The child knows that all buttercups are yellow, so there are three possible conclusions: the whole bouquet is yellow, or part of the bouquet is yellow, or none of the flowers in the bouquet are yellow. I found that up until nine years of age (and this was in Paris, so the children certainly did understand the French language) they replied, "The whole bouquet is yellow or some of my flowers are yellow." Both of those mean the same thing. They did not understand the expression, "some *of* my flowers." They did not understand this *of* as a partitive genitive, as the inclusion of some flowers in my flowers. They understood some of my flowers to be my several flowers as if the several flowers and the flowers were confused as one and the same class. So there you have children who until nine years of age heard every day a linguistic structure which implied the inclusion of a subclass in a class and yet did not understand this structure. It is only when they themselves are in firm possession of this logical structure, when they have constructed it for themselves according to the developmental laws which we shall discuss, that they succeed in understanding correctly the linguistic expression.

I come now to the fourth factor which is added to the three preceding ones but which seems to me to be the fundamental one. This is what I call the factor of equilibration. Since there are already three factors, they must somehow be equilibrated among themselves. That is one reason for bringing in the factor of equilibration. There is a second reason, however, which seems to me to be fundamental. It is that in the act of knowing, the subject is active, and consequently, faced with an external disturbance, he will react in order to compensate and consequently he will tend towards equilibrium. Equilibrium, defined by active compensation, leads to reversibility. Operational reversibility is a model of an equilibrated system where a transformation in one direction is compensated by a transformation in the other direction. Equilibration, as I understand it, is thus an active process. It is a process of self-regulation. I think that this self-regulation is a fundamental factor in development. I use this term in the sense in which it is used in cybernetics, that is, in the sense of processes with feedback and with feedforward, of processes which regulate themselves by a progressive compensation of systems. This process of equilibration takes the form of a succession of levels of equilibrium, of levels which have a certain probability which I shall call a sequential probability, that is, the probabilities are not established *a priori*. There is a sequence of levels. It is not possible to reach the second level unless equilibrium has been reached at the first level, and the equilibrium of the third level only becomes possible when the equilibrium of the second level has been reached, and so forth. That is, each level is determined as the most probable given that the preceding level has been reached. It is not the most probable at the beginning, but it is the most probable once the preceding level has been reached.

As an example, let us take the development of the idea of conservation in the transformation of the ball of plasticene into the sausage shape. Here you can discern four levels. The most probable at the beginning is for the child to think of only one dimension. Suppose that there is a probability of 0.8, for instance, that the child will focus on the length, and that the width has a probability of 0.2. This would mean that of ten children, eight will focus on the length alone without paying any attention to the width, and two will focus on the width without paying any attention to the length. They will focus only on one dimension or the other. Since the two dimensions are independent at this stage, focusing on both at once would have a probability of only 0.16. That is less than either one of the two. In other words, the most probable in the beginning is to focus only on one dimension and in fact the child will say, "It's longer, so there's more in the sausage." Once he has reached this first level, if you continue to elongate the sausage, there comes a moment when he will say, "No, now it's too thin, so there's less." Now he is thinking about the width, but he forgets the length, so you have come to a second level which becomes the most probable after the first level, but which is not the most probable at the point of departure. Once he has focused on the width, he will come back sooner or later to focus on the length. Here you will have a third level where he will oscillate between width and length and where he will discover that the two are related. When you elongate you make it thinner, and when you make it shorter, you make it thicker. He discovers that the two are solidly related and in discovering this relationship, he will start to think in terms of transformation and not only in terms of the final configuration. Now he will say that when it gets longer it gets thinner, so it's the same thing. There is more of it in length but less of it in width. When you make it shorter it gets thicker; there's less in length and more in width, so there is compensation—compensation which defines equilibrium in the sense in which I defined it a moment ago. Consequently, you have operations and conservation. In other words, in the course of these developments you will always find a process of self-regulation which I call equilibration and which seems to me the fundamental factor in the acquisition of logical–mathematical knowledge.

I shall go on now to the second part of my lecture, that is, to deal with the topic of learning. Classically, learning is based on the stimulus–response schema. I think the stimulus–response schema, while I won't say it is false, is in any case entirely incapable of explaining cognitive learning. Why? Because when you think of a stimulus–response schema, you think usually that first of all there is a stimulus and then a response is set off by this stimulus. For my part, I am convinced that the response was there first, if I can express myself in this way. A stimulus is a stimulus only to the extent that it is significant, and it becomes significant only to the extent that there is a structure which permits its assimilation, a structure which can integrate this stimulus but which at the same time sets off the response. In other words, I would propose that the stimulus–response schema be written in the circular form—in the form of a schema or of a structure which is not simply one way. I would propose that above all, between the stimulus and the response, there is the organism, the organism and its structures. The stimulus is really a stimulus only when it is assimilated into a structure and it is this structure which sets off the response. Consequently, it is not an exaggeration to say that the response is there first, or if you wish at the beginning there is the structure. Of course we would want to understand how this structure comes to be. I tried to do this earlier by presenting a model of equilibration or self-regulation. Once there is a structure, the stimulus will set off a response, but only by the intermediary of this structure.

I should like to present some facts. We have facts in great number. I shall choose only one or two and I shall choose some facts which our colleague, Smedslund, had gathered. (Smedslund is currently at the Harvard Center for Cognitive Studies.) Smedslund arrived in Geneva a few years ago convinced (he had published this in one of his papers) that the development of the ideas of conservation could be indefinitely accelerated through learning of a stimulus–response type. I invited Smedslund to come to spend a year in Geneva to show us this, to show us that he could accelerate the development of operational conservation. I shall relate only one of his experiments.

During the year that he spent in Geneva he chose to work on the conservation of weight. The conservation of weight is, in fact, easy to study since there is a possible external reinforcement, that is, simply weighing the ball and the sausage on a balance. Then you can study the child's reactions to these external results. Smedslund studied the conservation of weight on the one hand, and on the other hand he studied the transitivity of weights, that is, the transitivity of equalities if A = B and B = C, then A = C, or the transitivity of the inequalities if A is less than B, and B is less than C, then A is less than C.

As far as conservation is concerned, Smedslund succeeded very easily with five- and six-year-old children in getting them to generalize that weight is conserved when the ball is transformed into a different shape. The child sees the ball transformed into a sausage or into little pieces or into a pancake or into any other form, he weighs it and he sees that it is always the same thing. He will affirm it will be the same thing, no matter what you do to it; it will come out to be the same weight. Thus Smedslund very easily achieved the conservation of weight by this sort of external reinforcement.

In contrast to this, however, the same method did not succeed in teaching transitivity. The children resisted the notion of transitivity. A child would predict correctly in certain cases but he would make his prediction as a possibility or a probability and not as a certainty. There was never this generalized certainty in the case of transitivity.

So there is the first example, which seems to me very instructive, because in this problem in the conservation of weight there are two aspects. There is the physical aspect and there is the logical–mathematical aspect. Note that Smedslund started his study by establishing that there was a correlation between conservation and transitivity. He began by making a statistical study on the relationships between the spontaneous responses to the questions about conservation and the spontaneous responses to the questions about transitivity, and he found a very significant correlation. But in the learning experiment, he obtained a learning of conservation and not of transitivity. Consequently, he successfully obtained a learning of what I called earlier physical experience (which is not surprising since it is simply a question of noting facts about objects), but he did not successfully obtain a learning in the construction of the real structure. This doesn't surprise me either, since the logical structure is not the result of physical experience. It cannot be obtained by external reinforcement. The logical structure is reached only through internal equilibration, by self-regulation, and the external reinforcement of seeing that the balance did not suffice to establish this logical structure of transitivity.

I could give many other comparable examples, but it seems useless to me to insist upon these negative examples. Now I should like to show that learning is possible in the case of these logical–mathematical structures, but on one condition—that is, that the structure which you want to teach to the subjects can be supported by simpler, more elementary, logical–mathematical structures. I shall give you an example. It is the example of the conservation of number in the case of one-to-one correspondence. If you give a child seven blue tokens and ask him to put down as many red tokens, there is a preoperational stage where he will put one red one opposite each blue one. But when you spread out the red ones, making them into a longer row, he will say to you, "Now, there are more red ones than there are blue ones."

Now how can we accelerate, if you want to accelerate, the acquisition of this conservation of number? Well, you can imagine an analogous structure but in a simpler, more elementary situation. For example, with Mlle. Inhelder, we have been studying recently the notion of one-to-one correspondence by giving the child two glasses of the same shape and a big pile of beads. The child puts a bead into one glass with one hand and at the same time a bead into the other glass with the other hand. Time after time he repeats this action, a bead into one glass with one hand and at the same time a bead into the other glass with the other hand and he sees that there is always the same amount on each side. Then you hide one of the glasses. You cover it up. He no longer sees this glass but he continues to put one bead into it while at the same time putting one bead into the other glass which he can see. Then you ask him whether the equality has been conserved, whether there is still the same amount in one glass as in the other. Now you will find that very small children, about four years old, don't want to make a prediction. They will say, "So far, it has been the same amount, but now I don't know. I can't see any more, so I don't know." They do not want to generalize. But the generalization is made from the age of about five and one-half years.

This is in contrast to the case of the red and blue tokens with one row spread out, where it isn't until seven or eight years of age that children will say there are the same number in the two rows. As one example of this generalization, I recall a little boy of five years and nine months who had been adding the beads to the glasses for a little while. Then we asked him whether, if he continued to do this all day and all night and all the next day, there would always be the same amount in the two glasses. The little boy gave this admirable reply, "Once you know, you know for always." In other words, this was recursive reasoning. So here the child does acquire the structure in this specific case. The number is a synthesis of class inclusion and ordering. This synthesis is being favoured by the child's own actions. You have set up a situation where there is an iteration of one same action which continues and which is therefore ordered while at the same time being inclusive. You have, so to speak, a localized synthesis of inclusion and ordering which facilitates the construction of the idea of number in this specific case, and there you can find, in effect, an influence of this experience on the other experience. However, this influence is not immediate. We study the generalization from this recursive situation to the other situation where the tokens are laid on the table in rows, and it is not an immediate generalization but it is made possible through intermediaries. In other words, you can find some learning of this structure if you base the learning on simpler structures.

In this same area of the development of numerical structures, the psychologist Joachim Wohlwill, who spent a year at our Institute at Geneva, has also shown that this acquisition can be accelerated through introducing additive operations, which is what we introduced also in the experiment which I just described. Wohlwill introduced them in a different way but he too was able to obtain a certain learning effect. In other words, learning is possible if you base the more complex structure on simpler structures, that is, when there is a natural relationship and development of structures and not simply an external reinforcement.

Now I would like to take a few minutes to conclude what I was saying. My first conclusion is that learning of structures seems to obey the same laws as the natural development of these structures. In other words, learning is subordinated to development and not vice-versa as I said in the introduction. No doubt you will object that some investigators have succeeded in teaching operational structures. But, when I am faced with these facts, I always have three questions which I want to have answered before I am convinced.

The first question is: "Is this learning lasting? What remains two weeks or a month later?" If a structure develops spontaneously, once it has reached a state of equilibrium, it is lasting, it will continue throughout the child's entire life. When you achieve the learning by external reinforcement, is the result lasting or not and what are the conditions necessary for it to be lasting?

The second question is: "How much generalization is possible?" What makes learning interesting is the possibility of transfer of a generalization. When you have brought about some learning, you can always ask whether this is an isolated piece in the midst of the child's mental life, or if it is really a dynamic structure which can lead to generalizations.

Then there is the third question: "In the case of each learning experience what was the operational level of the subject before the experience and what more complex structures has this learning succeeded in achieving?" In other words, we must look at each specific learning experience from the point of view of the spontaneous operations which were present at the outset and the operational level which has been achieved after the learning experience.

My second conclusion is that the fundamental relation involved in all development and all learning is not the relation of association. In the stimulus–response schema, the relation between the response and the stimulus is understood to be one of association. In contrast to this, I think that the fundamental relation is one of assimilation. Assimilation is not the same as association. I shall define assimilation as the integration of any sort of reality into a structure, and it is this assimilation which seems to me to be fundamental in learning, and which seems to me to be the fundamental relation from the point of view of pedagogical or didactic applications. All of my remarks today represent the child and the learning subject as active. An operation is an activity. Learning is possible only when there is active assimilation. It is this activity on the part of the subject which seems to me to be underplayed in the stimulus–response schema. The presentation which I propose puts the emphasis on the idea of self-regulation, on assimilation. All the emphasis is placed on the activity of the subject himself, and I think that without this activity there is no possible didactic or pedagogy which significantly transforms the subject.

Finally, and this will be my last concluding remark, I would like to comment on an excellent publication by the psychologist Berlyne. Berlyne spent a year with us in Geneva during which he intended to translate our results on the development of operations into stimulus–response language, specifically into Hull's learning theory. Berlyne published in our series of studies of genetic epistomology a very good article on this comparison between the results obtained in Geneva and Hull's theory. In the same volume, I published a commentary on Berlyne's results. The essence of Berlyne's results is this: Our findings can very well be translated into Hullian language, but only on condition that two modifications are introduced. Berlyne himself found these modifications quite considerable, but they seemed to him to concern more the conceptualization than the Hullian theory itself. I am not so sure about that. The two modifications are these. First of all, Berlyne wants to distinguish two sorts of response in the S-R schema: (*a*) responses in the ordinary, classical sense, which I shall call "copy responses"; (*b*) responses which Berlyne calls "transformation responses." Transformation responses consist of transforming one response of the first type into another response of the first type. These transformation responses are what I call operations, and you can see right away that this is a rather serious modification of Hull's conceptualization because here you are introducing an element of transformation and thus of assimilation and no longer the simple association of stimulus–response theory.

The second modification which Berlyne introduces into the stimulus–response language is the introduction of what he calls internal reinforcements. What are these internal reinforcements? They are what I call equilibration or self-regulation. The internal reinforcements are what enable the subject to eliminate contradictions, incompatibilities, and conflicts. All development is composed of momentary conflicts and incompatibilities which must be overcome to reach a higher level of equilibrium. Berlyne calls this elimination of incompatibilities internal reinforcements.

So you see that it is indeed a stimulus–response theory, if you will, but first you add operations and then you add equilibration. That's all we want!

Editor's note: A brief question and answer period followed Professor Piaget's presentation. The first question related to the fact that the eight-year-old child acquires conservation of weight and volume. The question asked if this didn't contradict the order of emergence of the pre-operational and operational stages. Piaget's response follows:

The conservation of weight and the conservation of volume are not due only to experience. There is also involved a logical framework which is characterized by reversibility and the system of compensations. I am only saying that in the case of weight and volume, weight corresponds to a perception. There is an empirical contact. The same is true of volume. But in the case of substance, I don't see how there can be any perception of substance independent of weight or volume. The strange thing is that this notion of substance comes before the two other notions. Note that in the history of thought we have the same thing. The first Greek physicists, the pre-socratic philosophers, discovered conservation of substance independently of any experience. I do not believe this is contradictory to the theory of operations. This conservation of substance is simply the affirmation that something must be conserved. The children do not know specifically what is conserved. They know that since the sausage can become a ball again there must be something which is conserved, and saying "substance" is simply a way of translating this logical necessity for conservation. But this logical necessity results directly from the discovery of operations. I do not think that this is contradictory with the theory of development.

Editor's note: The second question was whether or not the development of stages in children's thinking could be accelerated by practice, training, and exercise in perception and memory. Piaget's response follows:

I am not very sure that exercise of perception and memory would be sufficient. I think that we must distinguish within the cognitive function two very different aspects which I shall call the figurative aspect and the operative aspect. The figurative aspect deals with static configurations. In physical reality there are states, and in addition to these there are transformations which lead from one state to another. In cognitive functioning one has the figurative aspects—for example, perception, imitation, mental imagery, etc.

The operative aspect includes operations and the actions which lead from one state to another. In children of the higher stages and in adults, the figurative aspects are subordinated to the operative aspects. Any given state is understood to be the result of some transformation and the point of departure for another transformation. But the pre-operational child does not understand transformations. He does not have the operations necessary to understand them so he puts all the emphasis on the static quality of the states. It is because of this, for example, that in the conservation experiments he simply compares the initial state and the final state without being concerned with the transformation.

In exercising perception and memory, I feel that you will reinforce the figurative aspect without touching the operative aspect. Consequently, I'm not sure that this will accelerate the development of cognitive structures. What needs to be reinforced is the operative aspect—not the analysis of states, but the understanding of transformations.

Reading List

NATURE OF SCIENCE

Bridgman, P. W. *The Logic of Modern Physics*, New York: Macmillan, 1927.

Bronowski, J. *Science and Human Values*, New York: Harper and Row, 1965.

Conant, James B. *On Understanding Science: An Historical Approach,* New Haven: Yale University Press, 1947.

Gabriel, M., and Fogel, S. (editors). *Great Experiments in Biology,* New Jersey: Prentice-Hall, 1955.

Holton, Gerald (editor). *Science and the Modern Mind, A Symposium,* Boston: Beacon Press, 1958.

Kuhn, Thomas S. *The Structure of Scientific Revolutions,* Chicago: University of Chicago Press, 1962.

Oppenheimer, J. Robert. *Science and Common Understanding,* New York: Simon and Schuster, 1954.

Roe, Anne. *The Making of a Scientist,* New York, Dodd, Mead, 1953.

Shamos, Morris. *Great Experiments in Physics,* New York: Holt, 1959.

Snow, C. P. *The Two Cultures and the Scientific Revolution,* New York: Cambridge University Press, 1959.

Weisskopf, V. *Knowledge and Wonder,* New York: Doubleday, 1962.

LEARNING PSYCHOLOGY AND ELEMENTARY SCHOOL SCIENCE

Almy, Millie, and Edward Chittenden, and Paula Miller. *Young Children's Thinking.* New York: Teachers College Press, 1966.

Brearley, Molly, and Elizabeth Hitchfield. *A Teacher's Guide to Reading Piaget,* London: Routledge and Kegan Paul, 1966.

Bruner, J. S. *The Process of Education,* Cambridge: Harvard University, 1960.

Bruner, Jerome. *Learning about Learning: A Conference Report,* Washington: United States Government Printing Office, 1966.

Flavell, J. H. *The Developmental Psychology of Jean Piaget,* Princeton: D. Van Nostrand, 1963.

Ford, G. W. (editor). *The Structure of Knowledge and the Curriculum,* Chicago: Rand McNally, 1964.

Gagne, R. M. *The Conditions of Learning,* New York: Holt, Rinehart and Winston, 1965.

Hunt, J. McV. *Intelligence and Experience,* New York: The Ronald Press, 1961.

Inhelder, Barbel, and Jean Piaget. *The Growth of Logical Thinking from Childhood to Adolescence,* New York: Basic Books, 1958.

Piaget, Jean. *The Child's Conception of Number,* London: Routledge and Kegan Paul, 1964.

————. *The Child's Conception of Physical Causality,* trans. Marjorie Babain. Paterson, New Jersey: Littlefield, Adams, 1960.

Piaget, Jean, and Barbel Inhelder. *The Child's Conception of Space,* trans. F. J. Langdon and J. L. Lunzer. London: Routledge and Kegan Paul, 1963.

Ripple, R. and V. Rockcastle. *Piaget Rediscovered,* Ithaca: Cornell University Press, 1964.

Smith, Herbert A. "Educational Research Related to Science Instruction for the Elementary and Junior High School: A Review and Commentary," *Journal of Research in Science Teaching,* I (1963), p. 199.

Vygotsky, L. *Thought and Language,* New York: John Wiley and Sons, 1962.

Whorf, Benjamin Lee. *Language, Thought, and Reality, Selected Writings of Benjamin Lee Whorf,* edited by John Carroll, Cambridge, Massachusetts: M.I.T., The Technology Press, 1956.

CURRENT CURRICULUM STUDIES IN SCIENCE

Fraser, Dorothy M. *Current Curriculum Studies in Academic Subjects,* Washington, D.C.: National Education Association, 1962.

Goodlad, John I., Renata von Stoephosius, and M. Francis Klein, *The Changing School Curriculum*, New York: The Fund for the Advancement of Education, 1966.

Heath, Robert W. *New Curricula*, New York: Harper and Row, 1964.

Hurd, Paul Dehart. *Theory into Action . . . in Science Curriculum Development*. Washington, D.C.: National Science Teachers, NEA. 1964.

Lockard, J. David (editor). *Report of the International Clearinghouse on Science and Mathematics Curricular Developments, 1966,* University of Maryland, 1966.

National Science Foundation. *Science Course Improvement Projects*, 1964.

Rosenbloom, Paul C. (editor). *Modern Viewpoints in the Curriculum*, Princeton: McGraw-Hill, 1964.

Schwab, Joseph J., and Paul F. Brandwein, *The Teaching of Science*, Cambridge, Massachusetts: Harvard University Press, 1962.

ELEMENTARY SCHOOL SCIENCE CURRICULUM PROJECTS

PROJECT TITLE: AAAS COMMISSION ON SCIENCE EDUCATION, WASHINGTON, D.C.

Brode, Wallace R. "Physical Science in the Early Elementary School," *American Journal of Physics*, XXXII (November 1964), 825–30.

Commission on Science Education. "Big Difference Between Knowing and Guessing," *Grade Teacher*, LXXXIII (January 1966), 76–79.

 "Process Method of Teaching Science," *Grade Teacher*, LXXXIII (January 1966), 60–74.

Gagne, R. M. "Elementary Science: A New Scheme of Instruction," reprinted in *Science,* CLI, No. 3706 (January 7, 1966) 49–53.

Livermore, Arthur H. "The Process Approach of the AAAS Commission on Science Education," *Journal of Research in Science Teaching*, II (1964), 271–82.

Walbesser, H. H. "Science Curriculum Evaluation: Observation on a Position," *The Science Teacher*, XXXIII (February 1966), 34–39.

PROJECT TITLE: ELEMENTARY SCHOOL SCIENCE PROJECT, UNIVERSITY
OF CALIFORNIA, BERKELEY, CALIFORNIA

Scott, Lloyd. "An Experiment in the Teaching of Basic Science in
the Elementary School," *Science Education*, XLVI (1962),
105–108.
——. "University of California Elementary School Science
Project: A Two-Year Report," *Science Education*, XLVI
(March 1962), 109–13.
——. "University of California Elementary School Science
Project: An Experiment in Diversity," *Journal of Research in
Science Teaching*, II (1964), 364–70.

PROJECT TITLE: ELEMENTARY SCHOOL SCIENCE PROJECT, UNIVERSITY
OF ILLINOIS

Atkin, J. Myron. "Elementary School Science Curriculum,"
Science Teacher (March 1960).
Atkin, J. Myron. "Science in the Elementary School," *Review of
Educational Research*, XXXIV (June 1964), 263–72.
——. "Some Evaluation Problems in Course Content Improve-
ment," *Journal of Research in Science Teaching*, I (1963),
129–32.
——. "Teaching Concepts of Modern Astronomy to Elementary
School Children," *Science Education* (February 1961).
——. "University of Illinois Elementary School Project—1964,"
Journal of Research in Science Teaching, II (1964), 328–29.
Pierce, Gail. "The University of Illinois Elementary School Science
Project: Report of the 1963 Writing Conference," *Journal of
Research in Science Teaching*, I (1963), 270–71.
Stecher, J. M. "Astronomy for Grades Five through Eight," *Science
and Children*, II (February 1965), 23–24.
Sutton, R. M. "Review of Three E-SSP Books," *Physics Teacher*,
III (February 1965), 82.
Wyatt, S. P. "University of Illinois Elementary School Science
Project," *Science Education News*, AAAS, LXII (1962), 14.

PROJECT TITLE: ELEMENTARY SCHOOL SCIENCE PROJECT, UTAH
STATE UNIVERSITY, LOGAN, UTAH

Braswell, A. L. "Science—A Humanity?" *The Science Teacher*,
XXXIII (April 1966), 32–33.

————. "Science for the First Grade," *Science and Children*, II (February 1965), 10–13.

Wood, J. K. "A Science Program for Elementary Grades," *Journal of Research in Science Teaching*, II (1964), 323–27.

————. "Elementary Science in the First Grade," *American Journal of Physics*, XXXII (November 1964), 830–31.

PROJECT TITLE: ELEMENTARY SCIENCE STUDY, NEWTON, MASSACHUSETTS

Duckworth, E. "The Elementary Science Study Branch of Educational Services Incorporated," *Journal of Research in Science Teaching*, II (1964), 241–42.

Hartley, Mary Lou. "Evaluation and Reflection after Attending the Elementary Science Study Summer School," *ESI Quarterly Report* (Winter and Spring 1964), 78–80.

Hawkins, David. "ESI Elementary Science Activities Project," *Science Education*, XLVIII (February 1964), 77.

————. "Messing about in Science," *Science and Children*, II (February 1965), 5–9.

Leodas, C. J. "The Elementary Science Study," *ESI Quarterly Report* (Winter and Spring 1964), 69–71.

Morrison, Philip. "Experiments in the Schoolroom," *ESI Quarterly Report* (Winter and Spring 1964), 63–68.

Morrison, Philip, and C. Walcott. "Enlightened Opportunism: An Informal Account of the Elementary Science Summer Study of 1962," *Journal of Research in Science Teaching*, I (1963), 48–53.

Moss, Penrod. "An Elementary Science Study Report from California," *ESI Quarterly Report* (Winter and Spring 1964), 81–82.

Nichols, Benjamin. "Elementary Science Studies—Two Years Later," *Journal of Research in Science Teaching*, II (1964), 288–92.

Whittlin, A. S. "Scientific Literacy Begins in the Elementary School," *Science Education*, XLVII (October 1963), 331–42.

PROJECT TITLE: ILLINOIS STUDIES IN INQUIRY TRAINING, UNIVERSITY OF ILLINOIS

Suchman, J. Richard. "Inquiry Training: Building Skills for

Autonomous Discovery," College of Education, University of Illinois (1961).

———. "Inquiry Training in the Elementary School," *The Science Teacher*, XXVII (1960), 42–47.

———. "The Illinois Studies of Inquiry Training," *Journal of Research in Science Teaching*, II (1964), 230–33.

PROJECT TITLE: MINNESOTA MATHEMATICS AND SCIENCE TEACHING PROJECT (MINNEMAST), UNIVERSITY OF MINNESOTA

Ahrens, R. B. "Minnemast—The Coordinated Science and Mathematics Program," *Science and Children*, II (February 1965), 16–18.

Rising, G. R. "Research and Development in Mathematics and Science Education at the Minnesota School Mathematics and Science Center . . . ," *School Science and Mathematics*, LXV, 811–20.

Rosenbloom, Paul C. "The Minnesota Mathematics and Science Teaching Project," *Journal of Research in Science Teaching*, I (1963), 276–80.

Subarsky, Z. "Communication—A Goal of Elementary Science Teaching," *Science and Children*, III (March 1966), 18–19.

PROJECT TITLE: SCHOOL SCIENCE CURRICULUM PROJECT, UNIVERSITY OF ILLINOIS

Salinger, R. F. P. "Progress Report: The School Science Curriculum Project," *Science Teacher*, XXXIII (January 1966), 37–39.

Shea, James H. "School Science Curriculum Project," *Geology Teachers Newsletter*, I (November 1964), 9.

PROJECT TITLE: SCIENCE CURRICULUM IMPROVEMENT STUDY, UNIVERSITY OF CALIFORNIA, BERKELEY, CALIFORNIA

Atkin, J. M., and R. Karplus. "Discovery or Invention?" *The Science Teacher*, XXIX (September 1962), 45–51.

Cunningham, J. D. "A Study of Children's Perceptual Rigidity," *Journal of Experimental Child Psychology* (1965).

———. "New Developments in Elementary School Biology," *American Biology Teacher*, XXVIII (March 1966), 193–98.

————. "Rigidity in Children's Problem Solving," *School Science Mathematics*, LXVI (April 1966), 377–89.

————. "The Einstellung Phenomenon in Children," *Journal of Experimental Child Psychology*, II, No. 3 (September 1965), 237–47.

Karplus, Robert. "Beginning a Study in Elementary School Science," *American Journal of Physics*, XXX (January 1962), 1–9.

————. "Chemical Phenomena in Elementary School Science," *Journal of Chemical Education* (May 1966).

————. "Meet Mr. O," *Science and Children*, I (November 1963), 19–24.

————. "One Physicist Experiments with Science Education," *American Journal of Physics*, XXXIL, No. 11 (November 1964) 837–39.

————. "One Physicist Looks at Science Education," in *Intellectual Development: Another Look*, Washington: Association for Supervision and Curriculum Development, 1964.

————. "Science Curriculum: One Approach," *Elementary School Journal*, LXII (February 1962), 243–52.

————. "The Science Curriculum Improvement Study," *Journal of Research in Science Teaching*, II (1964), 293–303.

Karplus, Robert. "The Science Curriculum Improvement Study— Report to the Piaget Conference," *Journal of Research in Science Teaching*, II, No. 3 (September 1964), 236–40.

————. "Teaching Physics in the Elementary Grades," *Physics Today*, XVII (October 1964), 34–38.

Karplus, Robert, and J. D. Cunningham. "The Free Fall Demonstration Experiment," *American Journal of Physics*, XXXI (1962), 656.

Powell, Cynthia Ann, and R. Karplus. "Objects Grab Bag," *Science and Children*, I (October 1963).

Reynolds, Jean, Cynthia Ann Powell and Robert Karplus. "Using a Bathroom Scale," *Science and Children*, I (February 1964).

Thier, Herbert D. "A Look at a First Grader's Understanding of Matter," *Journal of Research in Science Teaching*, III, No. 1 (1965), 84–89.

————. "First Step toward a New Elementary Science Curriculum," *Curriculum Letter,* Croft Educational Service (February 1966).

―――. "How Much? How Many? An Approach to Elementary Science," *The Instructor* (January 1966).

―――. "Quantitative Approaches to Elementary Science," *Instructor*, LXXV (January 1966), 65–67.

―――. "Science Education Supplement," *The Instructor* (January 1965).

―――. "The Involvement of Children in the Science Program," *Science and Children,* II (February 1965), 19–21.

Thier, H. D., and Robert Karplus. "Science Teaching Is Becoming Literate," *Education Age,* II (January–February 1966), 41–44.

Thier, H. D., and C. A. Powell and Robert Karplus. "A Concept of Matter for the First Grade," *Journal of Research in Science Teaching,* I (1963), 315–18.

Index

PRINTED IN U.S.A.

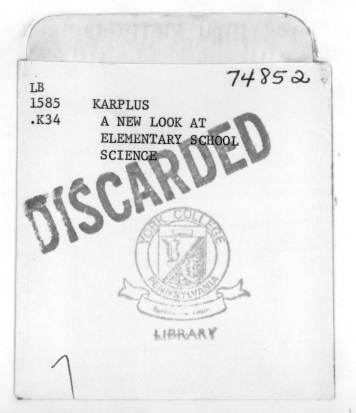